Denver
Now

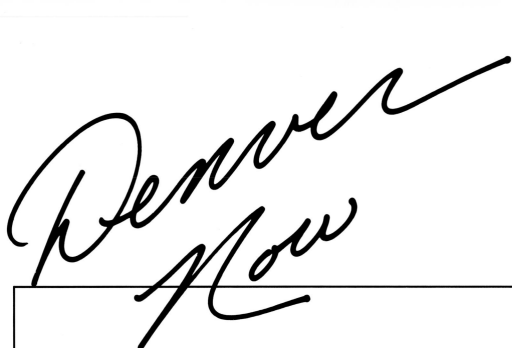

Denver Now

Publishers
David G. Heth
John D. Topping, Jr.

Director of Sales
Charles G. Whitley, Jr.

Business Manager
Julia K. Gatz

Editor
John Dunning

Senior Writer
Bruce W. Most

Contributing Writers
Ken Freed
Steve Perez

Proof Editor
Sharon Quigley McCann

Art Director
Valerie L. Thatcher

Assistant Artists
Kent Barnes
Chris Eaton
Meg Hogan
Donna Krasovec

Photography
Joe Chirichigno
T.W. Gaddy

Cover Photo
Greg Hill

Denver Now is published by Now Publications, Inc. Denver, CO. , copyright © 1982. No part may be reproduced in any form without the written permission of the publishers.

ISBN 0-943426-00-6

Library of Congress 81-85938

Denver's business showcase

Table of Contents

First Words

by John Dunning
Author of "Denver"

Denver looked like just another town that cold autumn day, and the Post might have been any newspaper where antiquated desks and typewriters and even some reporters were holdovers from the 1920s. But this was 1967; I was very young and Denver, by Western standards, was very old. The judgment of youth is often arbitrary, sometimes it is temporary, and usually it is harsh.

The assistant managing editor was an expert at grinding down impatient youth. He puffed stogies with an oval mouth and wore glasses and kept his hair cropped short. He might have been mistaken for a banker or a restaurateur, until he opened his mouth to speak. He could talk like a Marine drill sergeant when he had to, and he had to all day long. Now, without shifting his cigar, he calmly dismembered any vestige of hope that I might have brought in from the street.

"See that filing cabinet? It's full of applications. From the Washington Post. From the Wall Street Journal. From every big city on the East Coast. There are 500 active applications in there. We've got our pick of the best people in this country, so tell me why we should hire somebody like you. People are discovering Denver. This is the place to be. Everybody wants to come here, man, everybody. You gotta be good to beat out competition like that."

Later, because the Post was lurking in my tea leaves after all, I learned that this was a standard line he fed to everybody who asked for a job. How the Post actually hired people was the great mystery of the age, for they never seemed to draw on that wonderful filing cabinet filled with the hopes and prayers of harried Easterners. I was laughing about that one day when a Post old-timer leaned over and said, "Listen, kid, laugh at them all you want, but that part about the 500 applications is all true."

There really was a filing cabinet. It did (and probably still does) contain the files of hundreds of people who were just itching to get out of the rat race and come to Denver.

Why?

I climbed the iron steps to the gold-plated Capitol dome, and the climb seemed like the city itself: old-fashioned, archaic, a relic of the frontier. I walked around the dome and looked at the city from every angle, and it still looked like just another town, with a mean cold wind from the west and a main drag that pulled in all its awnings on Friday night and didn't open again till Monday morning.

I didn't know it then (how could I?), but Denver was already on the first step of its most recent and greatest Great Awakening. There had been others, going back to the 1870s, when the city's population quintupled in just ten years. But the growth of a city is like the growth of a child. You only notice it when you've been away a while, and Denver's growth had been coming along in fits and starts, with periods of calm stretching out like the peaceful parts of a good novel, between the highs.

All creative towns grow that way. That's probably a good thing, too, for if Denver had been growing from its beginnings in 1859 at the rate it's been going these past twelve years, we'd have the whole front range paved from Albuquerque to Montana, and Sterling would be a suburb.

But even in 1967 there must have been a whispering campaign, for people were finding Denver in spite of itself. They had heard of this metropolis on the plains where the mountains were fifteen minutes away, where the sun stayed out 300 days a year, where the climate was neither the sweatbox of Phoenix nor the icebox of Minneapolis. Even that ugly wind from the west had vanished by the time I hit the streets. It snowed that night, but by noon the next day the snow was gone without a trace and the temperature was creeping again into the high 60s.

People must have heard about that. They must have found out about our symphony orchestra and about the Broadway road shows that played regularly at the Auditorium. They knew about Elitch's ballroom, where big bandom was still alive and well.

They had heard of us in Washington, D.C., where politicians with millions of federal dollars were beating the bushes for towns like Denver. They had a monster growth portion to unleash on cities across the nation. The monster was called Urban Renewal, and its byproducts were sophistication and wrecking balls and big, big business.

Out came old Larimer Street.

Down came relics of the silver boom.

The Daniels and Fisher tower stood alone in a wasteland, like a pyramid in a desert.

We lost some good with the bad. Change is always like that. Some of those old buildings came out of the golden age of architecture. We lost the downtown movie palaces one by one: the RKO, the Denham, the Denver, the Centre. Elitch's ballroom was razed, and mourned by people who hadn't been there for years. For a while I thought all of lower downtown would become a parking lot.

Then the growth began.
With a vengeance.
With passion.
With single-minded dedication that by early 1981 could truly be called frantic.

When they were finished with the old town, and half finished with the new, it was apparent even to lifelong Denverites that all the old guidebooks were useless. This book is the first of a series of special guidebooks, a guide into the business community of the new Denver. It will tell you where to go for what you want. Business is the heart of any great city, and in Denver Now you'll find strong old companies in the same neighborhood with energetic youngsters. You'll find clear, honest descriptions of what they do and why they do it. You'll learn what services are available, what cultural pursuits, what avenues of leisure.

Denver Now is the kind of book that the city has long needed. Put together with great care by people who live here, it is dedicated to Denver's continued progress, where past and future can coexist and share a unique heritage and destiny.

Past, present and future. That's a toast even an old, cynical newsman can drink to.

Theatre & the Performing Arts

"Where there's art there's life," goes a slogan of the Denver Center for the Performing Arts. There's plenty of life in Denver, which offers a plethora of performing arts from symphony to legitimate theatre to modern dance. Choosing which to attend is the tough part so let our useful information help you.

Located in the foothills west of Denver near Morrison is one of America's most spectacular stages: Red Rocks, an acoustically perfect, natural open-air amphitheater carved out of red sandstone. On any given summer night you and 9,000 other spectators can gaze at the stars in the sky while listening to the stars on stage perform the best in jazz, country, or rock music. You can catch an inspiring sunrise on the plains during the annual Red Rocks Easter sunrise services (come early; people begin filling the seats at 3 a.m.). ↘ If man had been asked to build Red Rocks he couldn't have done a better job, though he might have done it more quickly. The red sandstone was laid down in seas 250 million years ago and raised 185 million years later along with the rest of the Colorado Rockies. A close inspection reveals fossils embedded in the two huge rocks that flank the tiered seats. ↘ Man did add finishing touches to nature's work in the late 1930s. Red Rocks Amphitheatre, or The Rocks as it is sometimes referred to, was officially dedicated in 1941 with a performance by Metropolitan Opera star Helen Jensen. ↘ Red Rocks continues a long tradition of performing arts and theatre in Denver. Even in the grubby, dangerous gold rush days theatre established a foothold. Denver's first theatre was on the second floor of a saloon and billiard parlor. It was an immediate success. ↘ Denver's golden age of theatre began in 1881 with the opening of Tabor's Grand Opera House at 16th and Curtis. Later, legitimate theatre faded somewhat as movies caught the public's fancy. Curtis Street became known in the 1920s as "Denver's Great White Way" so bright and numerous were the marquee lights. But by the 1960s those lights too had dimmed, and even the elegant Tabor fell to the wrecking ball. ↘ But a new artistic and cultural renaissance has begun to emerge at the foot of the Rockies. It is led by the huge Denver Center for the Performing Arts, located, appropriately, at the foot of Curtis Street. Ballet, classical music, jazz, new dance, opera, and theatre are finding a home here, enriching Denver's cultural maturity, rising out of the sea as Red Rocks did millions of years before.

DAN GRIEST

THE DENVER CENTER FOR THE PERFORMING ARTS

1245 Champa St.
893-4000

The reviews from across the nation are in. The audiences have spoken. The critical acclaim is unanimous. The Denver Center for the Performing Arts is a certifiable hit.

Rarely have the performing arts been brought together in one place with as much flair, flexibility, vision and inspiration. The Denver Center dominates four square blocks in the central business district of the city. The innovative architecture of the Helen Bonfils Theatre Complex and Boettcher Concert Hall has been blended masterfully with the historic Denver Auditorium Theater and Arena and the adjoining seven-story parking facility. The Galleria, a 60-foot-wide walkway covered by a soaring, arched glass canopy unites past and present and provides an open, airy plaza perfect for community events.

Each division of The Denver Center serves well its appointed art. And, like

any great work of art, the whole is greater than its parts. The Denver Center has provided a visual, artistic and financial lift to Denver. It has rejuvenated the community's commitment to the performing arts. It has become, in a very dramatic way, the proscenium arch to the Queen City of the West.

Nothing epitomizes The Denver Center's flexibility more forcefully than the Helen Bonfils Theatre Complex. A collaboration of artistic love between architects and experienced stage directors and producers, the elegant, visually exciting theatre encourages directors and actors to fulfill dramatic concepts impossible to do elsewhere.

Directors have two principal theatres to work with: The Stage and The Space. In The Stage, the 650 seats form a three-quarter circle around a great thrust platform, a design that dates to the Greek, Roman and Elizabethan traditions of theatre. With no seat further than 50 feet from the stage, an electric intimacy between actor and audience is created with each performance.

The Space has been called the "theatre of tomorrow." Its moveable seating holds up to 450 people and can be altered dramatically in shape and size, and its lighting and special effects capabilities are particularly adaptable.

A third theatre, The Lab, is an experimental 100-seat space that provides a pressure-free atmosphere that allows playwrights, directors and actors to refine their crafts.

The Helen Bonfils Theatre Complex is home to the Denver Center Theatre Company, the Rocky Mountain Region's own professional acting company. That the Company has found a dynamic, intimate, workable home is evident in the praise of such national publications as *Newsweek,* which reported, "The star of the Denver Center Theatre Company is the company itself."

Recognizing that the art of film was born and nurtured in America, design-ers of the Theatre Complex included the Denver Center Cinema, an integral and important complement to live theatre. With almost every film program, extensive background information enhances the viewers' enjoyment and provides the opportunity to learn more about the art of film itself. The main 255-seat auditorium is designed for comfort and has the best projection equipment available, enabling the Denver Center Cinema to show new prints of classic films.

The revolutionary Boettcher Concert Hall is the first fully surround concert hall in the United States. It opened March 4, 1978 to rave reviews. "Boettcher occupies a special place among American musical auditoriums," wrote *The New York Times'* Harold Schonberg. "The Hall can take anything an orchestra can deliver."

Within Boettcher, every element acts as an instrument to communicate music and contributes to the hall's acoustical purity. Even the seats serve as acousti-

cal elements. Each of the 2650 steam-bent high-backed plywood seats, none more than 85 feet from the stage, provides an additional musical presence for the listener and actually simulates the person sitting in it, so the acoustics are excellent regardless of audience size.

This masterful acoustical combination makes Boettcher an excellent forum for contemporary and vocal music as well as symphonic music.

Robert Garner's Center Attractions has placed Denver among the country's foremost cities in the eyes of touring theatre companies. Since 1961, Garner has produced more than 1,500 shows and created the highly successful "Best of Broadway" subscription series. Denver's geographical location provides an ideal stopover between the East and West coasts, and its growing subscription audiences have solidifed its place on the itinerary of major companies.

Denver's Auditorium Theatre where the "Best of Broadway" series is staged,

was the first and remains one of the last city-owned and operated theatres in the United States. Since opening in 1908, the theatre has undergone extensive renovation twice, making it suitable for use as an effective playhouse and concert hall. Long-range plans for future renovation of the Auditorium call for improvements in stage lighting, sight-lines and acoustics. Now linked by the soaring Galleria to the fresh, unique architecture of The Denver Center, the venerable Auditorium has taken on a new vigor and reputation as one of the country's most admired and enjoyable national theatres.

The Bonfils Theatre, at East Colfax and Elizabeth Street, opened in 1953. The first division of The Denver Center, The Bonfils offers community performers and audiences a complete and luxurious theatre facility fully equipped and staffed. Spacious, comfortable lobbies and a lounge and bar characterize the theatre's gracious atmosphere. The main auditorium seats 550 people.

At The Bonfils, however, it is the people who sustain the theatre's prestigious reputation. The professional staff provides a variety of quality entertainment while providing a showcase for the theatrical skills of those who work regularly in other professions. The programming at Bonfils has reflected the increasing strength and importance of minority theatre in America. Performance opportunities have been made available to actors of all cultures in every area of Bonfils programming.

Bo-Ban's Cabaret presents off-Broadway and revue works for a faithful and growing audience in a warm and friendly atmosphere of candlelight and cocktails. For many, Bo-Ban's has become "the most exciting little place in town."

The Bonfils Theatre for Children presents several plays each year, both traditional and new works, and provides a delightful introduction to theatre for Denver's youngsters. The productions, usually sold out well in advance, attract

more than 20,000 parents and children annually to weekend performances.

The addition of The Denver Center's two newest divisions, Denver Center Productions and the Audio-Visual Recording Division, have placed Denver in the forefront of the nation's performing arts community.

Denver Center Productions will produce original musicals and plays independently and in cooperation with other theatre organizations and individuals. A primary objective for Denver Center Productions will be to revive and preserve the best of the American musicals by working wherever possible with the artists who helped create the original productions. The project will bring the best work of composers like Richard Rodgers, Jerome Kern, George Gershwin, and Irving Berlin to the stage, then produce them for television utilizing the facilities of the Audio-Visual Recording Division.

The recording studio facilities of the Audio-Visual Recording Division will provide The Denver Center with the capability of recording productions in any of its facilities. Recordings of Denver Center productions will be carried on The Denver Center's own label.

The Audio-Visual Recording Division also will provide facilities for research and development of the most advanced audio and visual recording techniques in the industry.

The voice laboratory, under the leadership of Dr. Wilbur James Gould, internationally renowned laryngologist, will help improve the understanding of the voice in both professional and unprofessional capacities, and improve the quality of human voice performances in both areas. The voice laboratory will provide a pioneering study in high-altitude voice research.

The facility also will allow for advanced work in the field of digital recordings, a new era in recording. The new Audio-Visual Recording Division will be the first in the country to combine a research facility with a state-of-the-art recording studio as part of a performing arts complex.

13

WILLIAM K. SWARTZ

Denver Symphony Orchestra

One early, unconfirmed source places the date of the first concert in Denver as July 4, 1859. The story has it that a group of prospectors from Omaha played "Yankee Doodle"—and nothing else.

Musical groups and repertoires have progressed a bit since then.

Leading the way is the Denver Symphony Orchestra. In September 1981, the DSO began its 48th concert season. With a repertoire of 450 musical pieces, plans for the season called for the Denver Symphony to perform 54 classical concerts, 12 "Pops" concerts, eight free city concerts, six children's concerts, several public and private school concerts, college and university programs, and tiny tots concerts spon-

sored by the Junior Symphony Guild.

With 88 full time musicians, the Denver Symphony is classified as a major professional orchestra, one of 34 in the United States and Canada.

As music director and principal conductor, maestro Gaetano Delogu is responsible for selecting guest artists and conductors, along with a wide range of programs. DSO also boasts three other highly qualified conductors: Sixten Ehrling, principal guest conductor; James Rives-Jones, associate conductor; and Jim Setapen, Exxon/Arts Endowment conductor.

Typical of the music presented by the Denver Symphony is a recent concert: "Don Quixote, Fantastic Variations" and "Ein Heldenleben, Tone Poem,"

both by Richard Strauss and conducted by maestro Delogu. "Pops" and special concert guest artists for the '81-82 season include such renowned and diverse names as Peter Nero, Dottie West, Dave Brubeck and Victor Borge.

Home for the DSO is the beautiful, widely acclaimed Boettcher Concert Hall in the Denver Center for the Performing Arts.

But a beautiful home is only the beginning. Maestro Delogu's future plans call for continued improvement of the Denver Symphony Orchestra. He demands ever-higher artistic quality. When asked if the orchestra was up to fulfilling his requirements, the maestro replied, unequivocally, "Thank God, yes!"

1245 Champa St.
825-1298

Colorado Ballet Center
5305 E. Colfax Ave.
377-8074

There is a new air of excitement about the future of the Colorado Ballet. And much of that excitement swirls around a small spry man named Fernand Nault, who recently assumed the post of artistic director of the Ballet.

"I think the West is still big, so I dream big," says Nault. "There's no reason we can't have a ballet of equal stature with Ballet West, Houston, or Dallas." In fact, Nault strongly believes that this young company, the only professional ballet company in Colorado, can be molded into a group capable of a New York debut by 1985.

Nault brings impressive credentials to so bold a dream. He spent 21 years as a dancer and ballet master with the American Ballet Theatre and for a decade served as associate director and resident choreographer of Les Grands Ballets Canadiens, elevating that company to world renown. Nault believes that Denver audiences are ready for great ballet.

"Denver is growing rapidly," says Nault. "People here are thirsty to see good ballet—they want to learn."

A company of 21 professional dancers recruited from across the country, the Colorado Ballet performs with its own orchestra under the direction of James Rives-Jones at the Denver Auditorium and Boettcher Concert Hall. In addition to the company's own corps de ballet it features such guest artists as Gelsey Kirkland and Wayne Eagling. Founded in 1960 by Lillian Covillo and Friedann Parker as the Colorado Concert Ballet, the Ballet is also associated with the Colorado Ballet Center.

The Ballet's spectacular programs are mixtures of the classics and original modern works conceived especially for Colorado Ballet. The choreography reflects Nault's emphasis on conveying the emotional content as well as the technique of a ballet.

As a season subscriber you'll not only enjoy this theatrical experience, but you'll be entitled to a 20% discount on tickets, first choice of seats and performances (including the perennial Yuletide favorite, "Nutcracker"), backstage tours, rehearsal invitations, and other privileges. Subscribe now. Come feel the excitement of the Colorado Ballet.

COLORADO BALLET

GIBSON JAZZ

Paramount Theatre
579 16th St.

Ticket Information:
  Paramount Box Office
  Datatix Outlets in The Denver
  Or call 377-2757

Improvisation is the essence of great jazz—those deep emotions of love and lost love, sadness and happiness, infusing spontaneous, swinging sounds into every tune. Nothing nurtures and showcases improvisation better than Dick and Maddie Gibson's Jazz Concerts.

About every six weeks, from October through May, the Gibsons assemble individually ten outstanding jazz musicians exclusively for these Denver shows. Each concert is truly a unique event, bringing together musicians of outstanding reputation who have never

played together as a group. There are no rehearsals; in fact, the musicians usually meet only a short time before the show.

Because the musicians are carefully selected in terms of their talents, temperaments and styles, even with the absence of rehearsals the concerts invariably soar. Whether it's Count Basie's swinging "One O'clock Jump" or Duke Ellington's easy "In A Sentimental Mood," or a bop tune by Monk, the jazz sounds as if the musicians have been performing together for years. It works because each musician is a consummate professional, whether a young Emily Remler or a seasoned Clark Terry or Zoot Sims.

Most of all it works because Dick Gibson knows each musician personally, knows their styles and strengths, senses intuitively what combinations

will produce unforgettable jazz. Steeped in jazz since his early childhood, in Mobile on the Gulf Coast, Gibson has known jazz artists and booked jazz bands most of his life.

It is his life.

Only a few years old, the Gibson Jazz Concerts are already a Denver tradition. On both Friday and Saturday evenings, jazz aficionados frequently pack the resurrected and refurbished 2,100-seat Paramount Theatre, one of the city's historic movie palaces and a marvelous example of that architectural overkill, art deco.

But the concerts are not gaudy stage shows. They are music shows by musicians brought together to have fun, to create, to reach for the roots of jazz itself. Join them. Be spontaneous. Catch unforgettable jazz at the Gibson Jazz Concerts.

Paramount
Theatre

Paramount Theatre
519 - 16th Street
Denver, CO 80202
Box Office   534-5388
Executive Offices 534-5389

Sixteenth Street has seen a few opening nights in its time. Once the area bristled with magical, majestic theatres—the Denver, Centre, Orpheum, and not too far away, the Denham and the Broadway. Those proud palaces are gone: historic pieces of Denver's heritage sacrificed to "progress."

A sole sentinel remains — The Paramount.

Opening night excitement has returned to the Paramount. Denver's last grand movie palace breathes new life as a multi-use entertainment show-

place. The Paramount's Art Deco splendors are being restored by the Historic Paramount Foundation, a non-profit membership organization.

A prominent focal point on the Sixteenth Street Mall, the Paramount is the home of the renowned Gibson Jazz concerts, plays, dance and film presentations. It is the site of convention meetings, lectures, and social events. The Foundation also produces an annual family Christmas program in conjunction with the downtown Parade of Lights. A series of classic films is featured on July and August weekends.

Continued restoration of the lobbies, lounges, and auditorium will return the Paramount to its original design. Stage facilities will be improved for the increasing number of performances held

in the theatre. The Paramount's centerpiece, its twin console pipe organ, has been fully renovated. Again audiences can thrill to its resonant sounds. This mighty Wurlitzer is one of two double console theatre organs remaining in the United States. The other is in Radio City Music Hall.

Denverites have been enthralled with the organ, the gilt mouldings, the painted silk murals, the cut glass, and the plush appointments for more than fifty years. Again the marquee is lighted, a beacon proclaiming the Paramount's new life as an entertainment and convention facility.

The Paramount — attracting and thrilling new audiences and serving as a vital cog to the round-the-clock vigor of downtown Denver.

PRESENTS INC

If you were to guess the largest tenant of Denver's public facilities, you might name the Denver Broncos, or perhaps the Nuggets. But the undisputed owner of this title belongs to Feyline Presents, Inc.

Since Barry Fey founded it in 1967, Feyline has presented more than 2,000 attractions and drawn millions of spectators and fans. Feyline draws upon experience gained through years of success while maintaining a young and vital attitude. A pacesetter in the industry, Feyline stands out in every aspect of concert-event promotion, booking, and management.

The respect of performers and audiences alike has brought international recognition to Feyline's superior quality productions. Such acclaim was shown when Billboard Magazine named Barry Fey "Promoter of the Year" for an unprecedented three consecutive years— 1978, 1979, and 1980.

Feyline's "Summer of Stars" has rapidly become an anticipated tradition at Red Rocks Amphitheater and is recognized as the finest music series in the world. Considered the best outdoor facility in the country, Red Rocks' acoustics and natural ambience makes it a high point of top-name touring artists' itineraries, whether their forte is pop, rock, or country.

Feyline regularly offers such entertainers as Neil Diamond, Kenny Rogers, and The Who at McNichols Arena. Occasional concerts have packed Mile Hi Stadium and CU's Folsom Field in Boulder. Feyline has presented more performances by the Rolling Stones than any other promoter worldwide.

More intimate are presentations at the Rainbow Music Hall, the Boulder Theatre, and Mammoth Gardens, all Feyline showcases. Typical performers at those facilities have been Janis Ian and Manhattan Transfer.

A well-directed and organized company, Feyline has been spectacularly successful, possibly because it has maintained its youthful vigor. Modestly, Barry Fey shares the credit with the fans. "Denver audiences," he says, "are really unequalled."

Denver International Film Festival

1245 Champa
825-1897
For more information call
321-FILM

Each spring, in the month of May, the spotlights of the film world turn to Denver. It's the Denver International Film Festival, a delightful celebration of film and its creators and actors.

Growing remarkably in popularity and critical acclaim in only a few years, this non-profit film festival is already one of the largest of its kind, focusing on the outstanding films that for various economic reasons receive minimal commercial distribution.

Films from all over the world are offered at the Festival: Australia, Czechoslovakia, France, Ghana, India, Rumania, Sweden, the United States, West Germany, and many more nations. Many films are U.S. or world premieres. Virtually all are Denver premieres.

Nearly 150 films are screened, representing all types: contemporary, animation, classics, documentary, children's, regional, retrospectives, independents.

Receptions and seminars for filmmakers and stars dot the two-week affair. Personalities attending have included Lillian Gish, Robert Altman, Alan Alda, John Schlesinger, Anthony Quinn, and Laszlo Kovacs.

The agenda is studded with parties, workshops, seminars, premiere screenings, and other festivities for anyone who loves film.

The Festival also hosts events during the year, such as "Critics Choice" each fall, when national critics select a favorite film of the year and discuss their choices with audiences. There are such fundraising events as Willie Nelson's appearance for the world premiere of his film "Barbarosa," Academy Awards night, Vintage Ball, and a Halloween party.

Film Festival subscribers receive ticket discounts and other benefits, and are invited—free—to attend twelve Denver premiere screenings of new motion pictures.

It's a Festival any serious filmgoer won't want to miss.

LARRY LASZLO

the arvada center
for the arts and humanities

6901 Wadsworth
Arvada, CO 80003

Box Office
422-8050
Information Desk
431-3080

The Arvada Center for the Arts and Humanities is a special place. One of the few complete cultural centers in a city of Arvada's size, it is designed to provide facilities for the performing and visual arts as well as education and humanities programs. It includes theaters, studios, galleries and museum areas, conference and dressing rooms, and scene and costume shops.

Located on seventeen acres facing the mountains, the Arvada Center's open, flexible spaces help to create a warm, comfortable environment. It's ideal for traditional and innovative programs and offers a pleasant gathering place for people to enjoy, learn, and participate.

A full season of performing arts—dance, theater, music—is assured at the Arvada Center. The Arvada Center boasts two resident theater companies and two resident music ensembles.

The Arvada Center Theater Company, under the artistic direction of Jay Levitt, offers classic, contemporary, and musical productions. Recent programs included "Godspell", Jason Miller's "That Championship Season", and Neil Simon's "God's Favorite."

A company of players produces its own brand of participation theater for children. Typical presentations are "A Tale of a Frog Prince" and "Cinderella, Cinderella".

The Arvada Center is fully accessible to the handicapped, with ramps, wheelchairs and automatic doors. In keeping with this awareness, The Rocky Mountain Signers will provide interpreting for the hearing-impaired at various theater productions each season.

The Arvada Center Chamber Orchestra and The Arvada Center Chorale perform regularly throughout the year.

Resident companies and top national touring companies perform pops, dance, classical concerts and special events. Elizabeth Cotten and Mike Seeger, "Give 'Em Hell Harry," The Clarion Wind Ensemble, and The Joffrey Ballet were among the acts scheduled recently.

The Arvada Center Theater features a thrust stage in a comfortable auditorium seating 500. An outdoor amphitheater

seats over 1000. Both provide excellent sightlines and acoustics.

The Education Program at the Arvada Center offers a variety of learning experiences. Classes are offered in pottery, acting, ballet, photography, guitar, writing, jazz dance, painting, and much more. Nationally recognized artists speak and conduct workshops. A series of films, lectures, readings, and clinics round out a full educational program.

Fresh and exciting new art exhibits unfold monthly in the galleries of the Arvada Center. New work by local artists, watercolors, pottery, traditional Western art, and Laotian needlework are shown in Gallery programs offering imaginative and innovative artistic perspectives.

Changing exhibits in the Arvada Center Museum explore diverse themes in local history and other humanities areas. Visitors can view exhibits that draw upon collections of the Arvada Historical Society. Decorative arts and crafts from pre-industrial America also are featured. Highlighting the museum is the Haines log house, built in 1861. The earliest remaining home in Arvada, it is being developed to depict family life in an early frontier community.

Audiences and participants come to the Arvada Center from all over the metro area. It's a place of discovery, a place to create, to exchange ideas and learn. It's a place where every event draws a response and provides a reward. See for yourself—share in the excitement, the experience, the fun and enjoyment that is the Arvada Center for the Arts and Humanities.

Like most people, artists and performers need a home, a family, an environment that stimulates growth. Since 1968, The Changing Scene, Denver's experimental theatre and workshop, has provided that home.

Like the controversial mural that points out its entrance, "The Scene," as it's commonly referred to, is a risk-taking "people's" theatre. It has premiered the works and performances of contemporary playwrights, musicians, dancers, poets, actors, filmmakers, sculptors, puppeteers, painters, artists of nearly every description. More than 150 plays from around the world have premiered at The Scene, a good many of them going on to New York.

The Changing Scene is the creation of Alfred Brooks and Maxine Munt, two nationally known modern dancers who decided to move their studio from New York to Denver. Believing that theatre is the natural crucible for all the arts, they have opened their production facilities free of charge to striving artists. Their workshop, also free, provides an arena for the intermingling of ideas, the collaboration of film and video specialists, architects, painters, performers of all kinds. In addition, they have a full schedule of professional classes in modern dance.

This risk-taking spirit brought The Scene a grant from the National Endowment for the Arts in 1970, the only experimental theatre between Chicago and the West Coast so honored. Through the years they've received other grants and awards, including the prestigious Governor's Award for excellence in the arts, and grants from the Rockefeller Foundation. The Scene has

the CHANGING SCENE

helped nurture such artists as Cleo Parker Robinson, Martin Sherman, Gregory Biss, and Florence Bird.

The Changing Scene presents more than 20 productions a year. Admission for the public is minimal. The 76-seat theatre has a friendly, unpretentious, yet charming, flavor. On the way to the theatre the viewer passes through the gallery, usually displaying a series of paintings or sculptures. Espresso coffee is served during intermission. And the shows themselves—like the concept of The Changing Scene, are always exciting, controversial, original. The one thing they never are is dull.

Cleo Parker Robinson Dance Ensemble
THE NEW DANCE THEATRE, INC.

2006 Lawrence St.
893-2404

The Cleo Parker Robinson Dance Ensemble/New Dance Theatre school of dance is one of those pleasant surprises in the world of dance. They are a group of artists who have been critically acclaimed for their high powered energy on stage and their enthusiastic approach to instruction.

In the past decade the dance ensemble has achieved an international reputation under the direc-

tion of its gifted and dynamic choreographer, Cleo Parker Robinson. Colorado's first full-time professional modern repertory dance company, the ensemble has appeared to rave reviews in more than 500 performances and workshops worldwide. They were honored to perform in America's dance capital, New York City, as the first non-New York company to perform in the Harlem Cultural Council's *Dancemobile*.

Becoming more well known and equally exciting, is the company's New Dance Theatre school of dance in downtown Denver. Here, the widely applauded talents of the troupe's members, along with those of guest artists and

instructors, are available year-round to eager students of the dance. The school offers 20-plus classes per week, ranging from beginning to professional levels in modern, jazz, ballet, dancercise, and tap. Special children's classes emphasize exploration through dance of the mind and body and self.

Underlying both the school and the Dance Ensemble is a special sensitivity to the importance of the contributions of art to society. The school's emphasis on the study, understanding, and appreciation of the arts and of diverse cultural backgrounds is embodied on stage both in Robinson's dynamic choreography and the dancers' glorious individual expressions.

The Cleo Parker Robinson Dance Ensemble/New Dance Theatre: It's an artistic resource few cities in America have.

© MARGIE SOO HOO LEE

R. Paul Willett, Harvey Carey in scene from Arthur Miller's The Peace.

4201 Hooker St.
455-6077

Community theatre is largely a labor of love. Out of that love is often born great theatre, and such has been the tradition of the Gaslight Theatre under the guiding hand of R. Paul Willett.

The Gaslight has been referred to as the "best of what might be called Denver's Off-Broadway." It consistently offers a challenging mix of classics and modern Broadway fare, and has brought Denver such distinctive theatre as *That Championship Season, Ghosts, Slow Dance On the Killing Ground,* and *The Man Who Lost the River.*

"Plays should inform, entertain, instruct, and excite an audience," believes Willett, who is director, producer, actor, and maintenance man at the Gaslight. "I like controversy. If a play doesn't say anything, what have you got to think about?"

The 96-seat Gaslight Theatre is located in the basement of a large Victorian home. It is among the oldest continuing theatres in Denver, built in 1911 by Shakespearean actor George

Gaslight Theatre

Schwartz. The audience, embraced by muted red walls catching lamp glow, is so close to the stage they can almost reach out to touch the actors. Willett makes the most of this intimacy by selecting powerful, involving plays.

Like the Gaslight, Willett is steeped in theatrical tradition. A former children's acting coach in Hollywood and an intimate of several movie greats, Willett has been involved in theatre for over 50 years. He is a theatrical legend in Denver, founding the Lowry Players

during the Second World War. He has been guiding the Gaslight, today a non-profit corporation worthy of public contributions, since 1964. His invaluable contributions to Denver theatre have earned him the city's most prestigious honor, the Larry Tajiri Award.

Willett has also acquired a reputation for getting the most out of his actors, some of them having little or no acting experience. His results are abundantly evident in the exciting productions at Gaslight.

Tennessee Williams' In the Bar of a Tokyo Hotel

germinal stage denver

**For information call
572-0944**

Germinal Stage Denver is moving. After seven years as Denver's bright, intimate experimental playhouse, the renovated warehouse theatre is destined for the wrecking ball.

But Ed Baierlein, co-founder and director/manager, has been seriously looking for a new location for what has long been one of Denver's best small theatres.

The search should be successfully concluded, and the Germinal relocated, by the beginning of 1983.

The theater's name is eminently appropriate. "I always felt we were seed-like," says Ed Baierlein. "And I wanted an image as experimental, a forward-looking theatre company."

Germinal Stage appeals to the theatrically adventurous. Since November 1974, when 66 patrons saw the first performance of *The Entertainer,* more than 40 productions have been staged in the Market Street warehouse. The 66 customers have grown to 1000 subscribers who keep coming back. But with the new location Ed Baierlein is looking for new directions.

"We could continue to do the things we have been doing. But artistic growth is essential. The trick is to be experimental *and* popular."

Germinal Stage Denver has set out on a new voyage of discovery. As in the past, we're sure Denver will come along.

LORETTO HEIGHTS THEATRE

3001 S. Federal
936-8441

"The undergraduate cast in the play performs theatrical magic."

"It is college theatre at its best."

These are just two of the many rave reviews received over the years by the Heights Theatre of Loretto Heights College. Producing the best shows from Broadway, Off-Broadway, and the classics, the Heights Theatre has brought Denver such plays as "The King and I," "My Fair Lady," "Macbeth," "Cabaret," and "The Birds."

It's live theatre at its best, for less than the cost of a first-run movie. For a few dollars more you can enjoy a delicious pre-performance buffet din-

ner in the elegant surroundings of the May Bonfils Room adjoining the theatre. The Heights Theatre is housed in the Bonfils-Stanton Center for the Performing Arts, located in the college's beautiful 100-acre campus. Theatre is one of

the several performing arts majors at the college, along with dance, music, and other programs. In addition, the college offers majors in fine arts, humanities and sciences, teacher education, nursing, and business.

The school's innovative University Without Walls is designed for adults whose work, family, and professional responsibilities make it difficult to participate in a traditional academic schedule.

With 800 students from across the country and the world, Loretto Heights College, along with its theatre and other programs, is making an impressive contribution to the educational and cultural life of Denver and Colorado.

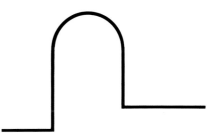

SHWAYDER THEATRE

**Jewish Community Center
Leetsdale & Dahlia
399-2660**

Over the centuries the Jewish contribution to the world's performing arts has been colorful, diverse, and vast, and the world is richer for it. The Shwayder Theatre at the Jewish Community Center has become Denver's showcase for that remarkable and continuing contribution.

"We try to search out our roots through the performing arts," explains Evelyn Tucker, co-director with Merrily Wallach. "The performing arts have always been an important part of our background as a creative people who have wandered and searched for a home. Many of America's best-known Jewish playwrights—Arthur Miller, Neil Simon, and others—put a sensitivity into their Broadway plays that we try to draw out in our own special way."

"The Shwayder offers a great variety of productions," says Merrily Wallach, "from plays and film festivals to guest artists and lecturers." There is also the Theatre Academy offering classes to children and adults in drama, mime, dance, and voice.

The co-directors bring years of experience teaching, acting, and directing to building the Shwayder into one of the city's strongest community theatres. Evelyn Tucker has directed and taught acting in Denver for the past 17 years. She previously has acted in summer stock and directed off-Broadway shows. Merrily Wallach has appeared in theatre, TV movies, and commercials, and for 20 years directed the Children's Traveling Theatre for the National Council of Jewish Women.

They are able to produce their shows in one of the city's most beautiful theatres. Its Greek-style setting seats 301 people. The high-rise seats offer excellent viewing of the thrust stage from every location. The Shwayder is also available for rentals. All inquiries should be made to 399-2660, extension 467.

Through the talented energies of these two women it is hoped Shwayder Theatre will never have a dark night.

HERITAGE SQUARE
OPERA HOUSE

**For more information call
279-7881**

If you're in the mood for unabashed fun, hilarous entertainment, and delicious food all under one roof, G. William Oakley's Heritage Square Opera House is your answer.

This is dinner theatre like you've never seen before—and you'll never forget. The heart and ham of it is their outrageously "revised" melodramas—classic melodramas the likes of "Billy The Kid" or "Dr. Jekyll and Mr. Hyde" turned upside down by the hilarious pen of G. William Oakley.

Come prepared to participate. Following a preshow silent movie program, the Opera House's top flight professional cast leads the audience in practicing booing and hissing the villain and cheering the hero and heroine. The show itself will reduce you to tears of laughter, and afterwards the cast presents vaudeville comedy bits, ragtime music, and audience sing-along.

All this insanity follows a scrumptious and ample buffet featuring a variety of salads, roast beef, ham, fried chicken, potatoes, and other entrees and side dishes. Drinks are available before and after the show in the upstairs lounge.

The friendly, courteous staff is always there to serve you. And if you're looking for something different for a luncheon, reception, or business meeting, Heritage Square Opera House can fill your needs.

The turn-of-the-century Victorian decor of the elegant dining room, theater, and other rooms matches the flavor of the entertainment. The Opera House itself is located in a recreated Victorian village with general store, metalsmith, and shops where artisans sell their wares.

Turn back the pages of time for an afternoon or evening of entertainment. If you don't have fun at the Heritage Square Opera House, you won't have fun anywhere.

central city opera

Box Office
623-7167

She stands like a grand old lady near the heart of Central City. Her two-story, stately stone presence remains as dignified and graceful as the day she was born in 1878.

She is the Central City Opera House, birthplace of culture in Colorado and today a magnet for many of the world's finest operas and opera stars. Her renowned Central City Summer Festival, presenting great opera and all of the performing arts, draws thousands each summer. *Time* magazine has praised the festival as "One of the finest small musical festivals in the country."

When the Cornish and Welsh gold miners built the remarkable mid-Victorian opera house, they insisted on acoustical and visual perfection. After the gold ran out and the house darkened, she was brought to life again by spirited visionaries who meticulously restored her inherent beauty and glory.

When the Opera House reopened in 1932 she did so with the best: Lillian Gish in *Camille.* Other stars followed: Cyril Ritchard, Ruth Gordon, Shirley Booth, Helen Hayes, Beverly Sills. Central City staged the classics and created her own, premiering, for instance, the now-famous *Ballad of Baby Doe.* The Festival grew in ambition as well as quality, adding dance and jazz and such extras as Victorian salon recitals, The Composers Series featuring works in progress, historical tours, and the world premiere of the "cabaret-opera," *The Face on the Barroom Floor*.

Her infectious spirit of revitalization spread to all of Central City. The same visionaries who restored the Opera House transformed the once-opulent 1872 Teller House into a unique museum and four entrancing dining rooms. The 1874 Chain O'Mines Hotel is a charming and functional place for visitors. And Central City herself has been designated a Registered National Historic Landmark, a living monument to the fascinating blend of dirty, dangerous mining and high culture of the late 1800s.

At the heart of it all is the Central City Opera House. Over a century ago she brought music to the mountains. Today she brings music to the world.

Dana Krueger as Mrs. Tabor in the Central City Opera production, Ballad of Baby Doe.

Art & Antique Galleries

Although not much more than 100 years old, Denver is rich in art and antiques. Whether you're seeking premium 17th century English furniture or contemporary lithographs by Colorado artists, you'll find it among these exclusive shops.

Romanticized on stage, screen and in books, "The Unsinkable" Molly Brown is firmly established in Western folklore. Like all legends, Molly's real life was never quite as magical as we like to believe. Molly did marry a wealthy Colorado miner, J.J. Brown. She lived in a fashionable home with a red room and a golden stairway. And she most certainly saved lives on the sinking Titanic. But unlike the legend, Molly never was accepted by Denver's high society. Her marriage failed. And she died in obscurity. ❧ But Molly's feisty, irreverent spirit is preserved in the home that J.J. Brown bought for her. Built in 1889 from Colorado limestone, this lovely 3-story, 18-room residence in the prestigious Capitol Hill area today ranks as one of Denver's most popular tourist attractions. Daily tours enthrall the curious with stories of Molly's doings while guiding them through rooms filled with beautiful period (1890-1910) furniture, rugs, silver, glassware, tapestries, and clothing. ❧ (Tours of Molly's home, 1340 Pennsylvania St., are given daily from 10-4, and Sundays from 12-4. The home is closed Thanksgiving, Christmas, New Year's, and Mondays from Labor Day to Memorial Day.) ❧ One of Denver's most beautiful examples of Victorian architecture, Molly's home embodies the spirit of preservationism which has been kindled here in recent years. Molly was something of a preservationist herself, having led a drive to save the Denver cottage of poet Eugene Field. Her own home almost fell to the wrecking ball in 1970 before a hastily-formed Historic Denver, Inc., saved it. ❧ Today, neighborhoods such as Capitol Hill and Curtis Park are refurbishing homes, while commercial ventures are renovating structures like the old Tivoli Brewery and the D&F Tower. ❧ This booming city of the future has come to recognize the importance of preserving the dignity and heritage of the past that made it the city it is today. ❧ Molly would be damned proud.

Trapline, *a bronze sculpture by Hollis Williford*

Carson Gallery of Western American Art

The Equitable Building
730 17th Street
573-5938

The true value of Western art has little to do with the appraised worth of a piece, says Tom Carson, owner of the Carson Gallery of Western American Art. A work of art in your home or office is an extension of yourself, a statement of your identity; so the first consideration when buying art is the investment in pleasure and enjoyment that the work of art will give you in years to come.

"We look for honesty in an artist," Carson says. "We look for artists with something valuable to say, who say it with talent, expertise, conviction, knowledge of their craft, and unique expression."

Carson Gallery deals as much in emotion as art. For example, the bronze sculpture "Trapline" by Hollis Williford reveals more than a lone trapper sludging through winter snows with his rifle slung on one shoulder; the work is a study in perseverance.

The same kind of impact is inherent in all the works displayed at the Carson Gallery, be they sculptures by Kent Ullberg or Peter Fillerup; or paintings by James Disney, Bev Doolittle, Charles Wysocki or Tucker Smith. Any of these nationally known artists delivers both emotional and material worth to the owners of their works.

The art in the Carson Gallery yearns to be lived with, contemplated and absorbed to have the fullest effect. But not all of the works find their way into homes. The Carson Gallery also helps place art in business settings. The gallery will work with office planners and business management to select and display precisely the right pieces of American art to fit any decor. The result is a more distinctive office, promoting a personal corporate image, boosting employee morale, providing an enjoyable environment and a sound business investment likely to increase in value.

Along with sculptures and paintings, the gallery also features Native American jewelry, each piece distinctively styled for sophisticated tastes. Carson Gallery is the region's exclusive showroom for Renaissance Studios Ltd., importers and restorers of fine English and continental antique furniture for home or office.

The gallery is notable in itself. Located in the historic Equitable Building at 17th and Stout Streets in the heart of the financial district downtown, the gallery is appointed with rich cherry wood paneling, plush green carpets, and careful lighting to display each work of art to its best advantage. "We take great pride in what we're presenting," Tom Carson says. "We want people to come in to browse, recognizing that walking through our gallery is like taking a trip through the country we love."

gallery one

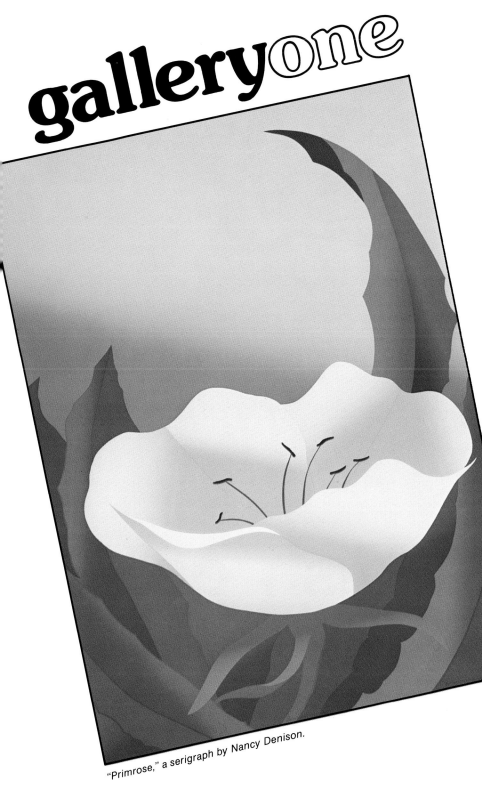

"Primrose," a serigraph by Nancy Denison.

 # inkfish gallery

1810 Market
893-8205

"We've been collecting for over 20 years," says Paul Hughes, co-owner with his wife, Nancy, of Inkfish Gallery. "What we sell is what we collect and believe in."

What Paul and Nancy believe in most passionately are contemporary Colorado artists, though they carry many nationally known artists as well.

Offering abstract art in all mediums, Inkfish is the major outlet for the paintings and serigraphs of Coloradan Dave Yust, the watercolors of Sandra Kaplan Dragul, the mixed media and pastels of Mark Dickson. And it's the best place to find the works of that fixture of Colorado art, Vance Kirkland. They carry his watercolors, drawings, and oils from his first works in 1928 to the present.

Among the internationally known artists represented at Inkfish are Bertoia, George Rickey, and Richard Anuszkiewicz.

The Hughes have been entwined with the growth of Colorado art for years. Paul served as curator of the Alliance for Contemporary Art Auction; and Inkfish does a good deal of publishing, helping Colorado artists to gain exposure and an avenue for marketing their works.

Inkfish provides complete art consulting services. Says Paul: "We work through designers, architects, and other art consultants to provide the specific look that best serves an interior design, whether commercial or residential."

As with many other established businesses in the changing downtown, Inkfish may be relocating in the near future so please inquire before visiting.

SEBASTIAN-MOORE GALLERY

1411 Market St.
534-5659

Since its opening in 1977, the Sebastian-Moore Gallery has been much more than a place to hang and sell contemporary art. It has been among the leaders in stimulating the revitalization of the arts in the Denver area.

Under the creative ownership of Christy Sebastian and Mimi Moore, the gallery was among the first to start commercial development of the Market Street area of lower downtown. It was the first gallery to commit itself exclusively to contemporary art.

The gallery has formed an influential and highly refined stable of regional artists whom it represents and promotes exclusively. It has brought to Denver's attention national artists of the stature of Robert Rauschenberg, David Hockney, and Jasper Johns to name a few.

Sebastian-Moore is also the only gallery in the city outside the Denver Art Museum to mount major exhibitions such as Post Minimal art, New Realism, and architectural drawings.

Recognizing that business collections are fundamental to the support of the arts, the gallery consults closely with commercial clients, designers, and archi-tects. Knowledgeable consultation on investment, installation, and building a collection is available to the individual as well.

The flexibility of the gallery's space has enabled it not only to mount impressive exhibitions but to host fund-raisers, recitals, and performances for groups like Cleo Parker Robinson and the Denver Symphony Orchestra. The gallery also has held classes in contemporary art history, film, and creativity in conjunction with area colleges and universities.

The Sebastian-Moore Gallery. Committed not only to the finest in contemporary art, but to better arts for Denver.

1440 Larimer Street
623-3874

Contemporary Southwestern art has become increasingly popular across the country the last few years, and in no small way it's been due to the vigorous efforts of Ken Phillips Fine Arts gallery.

This is not cowboy-and-Indian art, but contemporary, sophisticated, modern visions, seen through the eyes of Western artists like Earl Biss, R.C. Gorman, Ed Singer, Frank Howell, Veloy Vigil, Presley LaFontaine, John Suazo, and others.

"I believe Southwest art is one of the most communicative artistic forms—providing many levels of interpretation," says Ken, who has been involved with art all his life.

Ken's gallery has focused the attention of collectors toward many artists, and today he offers one of the largest and finest selections of work by notable contemporary Southwestern artists. Ken Phillips does Earl Biss' publishing, and the gallery is the primary national outlet for Biss' work.

Another specialty is framed and unframed graphics of originals and sculptures carved in fine alabaster marble mined in Colorado.

If you're unfamiliar with the beauty and expression of contemporary Southwestern art, the salespeople at the gallery are able to provide personal insights into the works. They are intimately familiar with the artists, many of whom frequent the gallery.

Earl Biss' Kiowas in Crow Country

Yippy Yi Yo *by Dan Allison*

blue door II gallery

Regatta Plaza
3150-G S. Peoria St.
Aurora
695-0123

Great art startles our perceptions . . . provokes our thoughts . . . captivates our sensibilities and often brings new realizations.

Provoking our thoughts and inspiring new appreciation is all in the scheme of things at James Robischon's Blue Door II Gallery.

"I try to stimulate people through my exhibitions," says Robischon, who has been the director at Blue Door II since 1976 and has become well known for his untiring support and promotion of art in the area. "I try to expose people to the best art possible and that can often be very challenging. Quality is my foremost concern."

There's an exciting sense of high spirit about the place. It has a wonderfully diverse atmosphere, refined one moment and funky the next. There are hand-cast creations, paper, lithographs, silk screens, life-size sculptures, ceramic objects, posters (some very rare), and realistic and abstract paintings.

One never knows what to expect from month to month, for the gallery features the freshest in today's art. It could be an exhibition of new trends in photography, a survey of regional print makers, a one-artist show or any theme from humor to romance.

At the Blue Door II Gallery, Robischon presents the promising and the prominent in contemporary art. He is not smit-ten by "brand name" artists, is not afraid to explore the controversial, or to exhibit the overlooked or the undiscovered.

The commitment is always to excellence and to surprisingly affordable prices. "I have never believed that fine art is only for the affluent," says Robischon. He helps guide novices whose tastes may be purely decorative as well as assisting collectors, corporations, and museums with their collections.

Robischon has been a picture framer for 14 years. His in-house custom framing service is known for its reasonable prices and ability to handle all types of art work.

After almost six years in Aurora, Robischon may be relocating in the metro area in the near future.

carson·sapiro

1411 Market
623-4051

There is much to see in the art world—tapestries, paintings, photographs, drawings, ceramics, glassworks and limited edition prints. The "visual overload" could be confusing. With the demand for fine art, cautious judgment is needed. Carson-Sapiro Art Consultants and Gallery provides individuals and businesses with experienced advice in choosing one piece of art or an entire collection. They enjoy making the art selection process interesting and pleasant.

The spacious gallery features established regional and national artists, but takes pride in new-talent discoveries as well. The shows are exciting with the emphasis on significant artists and new trends in a variety of mediums. Clients are always welcome to browse and chat about the art as well as to view art works in the extensive inventory.

An expert staff of seven collaborates with clients and with architects and designers to select distinctive art that fulfills aesthetic and budgetary requirements. Personalized service is extended and includes everything from commissioning specific art works to supervising installations and framing.

What has made Carson-Sapiro Art Consultants and Gallery a significant art source for the region has been the ability to generate enthusiasm for quality contemporary art. It isn't difficult to get others involved when one is so committed oneself.

This fine gallery may be relocating soon, so please give them a call before visiting.

Many Winters *by Dane Clark*

DRISCOL
Gallery

555 17th St., Suite 160
623-5520

Like the land it depicts, Western art is an unsurpassed panorama of beauty and diversity.

It is this and more.

It is a spirit of Western man, and of animals who roamed those mountains and prairies before man came.

Driscol Gallery offers the best of this Western art by contemporary artists in its bright, airy, two-level gallery in the Fairmont Hotel.

Displayed here are the elemental bronze sculptures of Ken Bunn, the powerful bronze animals of Veryl Goodnight, the lovely direct line etchings of Sandy Scott, the Southwestern landscapes of Walt Gonske, the subtle texture of Chester Comstock's bronze birds, and many, many more works by a wide range of contemporary artists.

Owners Pam Driscol and Deane Knox have earned the confidence of private collectors and corporations alike in matters of procurement, curation, and appraisal. Their knowledge is widely respected, their ties strong to many of the most recognized artists in the United States. This intimate expertise enables them to obtain works from distant corners of the country, and adds immeasurably to the always-fine pieces on display in their own gallery.

Their enthusiasm prompted the organization of the distinguished, immensely successful Peking Exhibition of American Western Art, which presented a rich and diverse image of the American West through all types of media.

Western art indeed is an art that knows no boundaries and no time. Driscol Gallery is your step-off point.

ARCTIC ART

Market Street Mall
1325 18th St.
893-5407

Hours: Tues.-Sat. 11 am-5 pm

Cherry Creek North
2817 E. 3rd Ave.
320-0469

Hours: Mon.-Sat. 10 am-5:30 pm

When Brigitte and Paul Schluger lived in Canada several years ago, they became enthusiastic and dedicated lovers of Eskimo art. They found a rich culture in sculpture and prints, a world of imagination and harsh reality. It was important, neglected art: a pictorial record of the Eskimo and his world.

Brigitte and Paul brought this fascination to Denver in the mid-seventies. Wanting to share the subtle beauty of the Eskimo's art, the Schlugers opened their gallery, Arctic Art, in 1975. They have been in the same location at 1325 18th Street (18th & Market Streets

in the Market Street Mall) for seven years and are now very pleased to announce a partnership with Carol Weil and, as of June 1, 1982, a second location at 2817 E. Third Avenue

Arctic Art specializes in antique and contemporary Eskimo art. As official representatives of the Canadian Eskimo Cooperatives, they have access to the finest artistic creations from these northern peoples. For example, Arctic Art features the region's largest collection of Eskimo sculpture in soapstone, bone, and ivory.

Much of the art work shown in Arctic Art is based on Eskimo myths and legends. Exquisitely detailed ivory, soapstone, and bone sculptures of birds, seals, walruses, bears, humans and spirit beings convey the Eskimo's view of life and the afterlife. These themes are echoed in the many early and recent stencils, stonecuts, engravings and lithographs by the print-making Eskimo communities at Cape Dorset, Baker Lake, Holman Island and elsewhere in the Canadian Arctic.

Such recognized Eskimo print makers

as Kenojuak, Kalvak, Oonar, Pudlo and others use traditional skills to produce exciting contemporary art. The prints are bold, highlighted with vibrant colors and clear lines. The works have a whimsical and innocent quality that is entirely captivating.

And the Schlugers have made a major effort to collect prehistoric artifacts of the Eskimo culture, as well as lime grass and birch bark baskets from the coastal regions, and caribou masks from the mountainous areas. A good selection of Eskimo dolls also is on display at Arctic Art, along with recently acquired Eskimo tapestries.

Arctic Art provides complete print-framing services. They will search for rare and unusual works, and they offer appraisal services for individuals and corporations.

Brigitte and Paul Schluger are proud of their record of working successfully with Eskimo art collectors all over the United States and Canada. Together with Carol Weil they look forward to many more years of offering the best in Eskimo art.

HILLS GALLERY

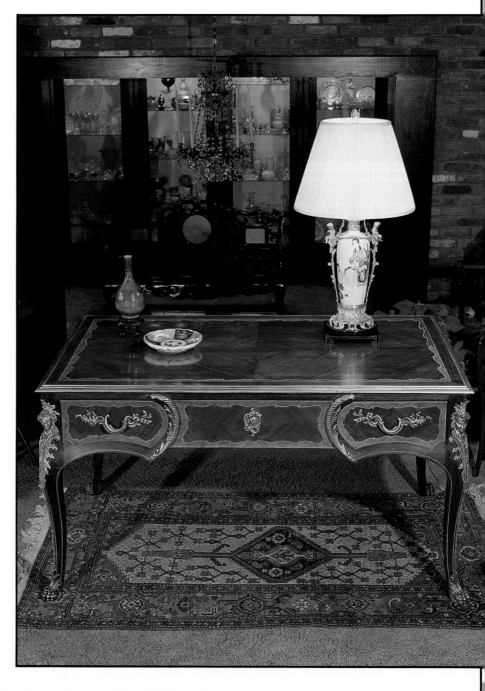

McKINLEY & HILL

4340 Harlan
424-1102

Among people who love and collect quality antiques McKinley & Hill is something of a legend in Colorado. For two decades they have offered some of the finest in English, American, and French formal and country furniture from the 17th, 18th, and early 19th century, as well as Victorian art glass and cut glass, Oriental porcelain, Wedgwood, silver, and pewter.

A visit to this Wheat Ridge gallery is worth the trip in itself. The huge, stunningly decorated 1890s Georgian-style farmhouse was enlarged a few years back and serves as both gallery and home to partners Bud Hill and Hogue McKinley. It's as original and pleasing (they designed the addition themselves) as the gallery's contents.

It's quickly apparent as you browse through the gallery that McKinley and Hill brings the classicist's eye to the richly eclectic yet compatible pieces. A French Louis XV-style bureau may stand next to an impressive display of 18th century blue and white Canton. Or an English Regency mahogany davenport—captain's desk—with slide and lift-up leather top may shadow Imari (Japanese) porcelain.

Widely respected for their vast knowledge of antiques, the two men were instrumental in founding the Colorado Antiques Dealers Association and the National Antiques Dealers Association. In addition to a marvelous selection of antiques, McKinley & Hill Antiques offers expert appraisals of antiques and interior design services.

Ayers
of franktown

**Located between Denver
and Colorado Springs
6 miles east of Exit 182, Interstate 25
Franktown, CO 80116
688-3827**

By appointment, Monday-Saturday

In the galleries of Ayers of Franktown, the impact of *great* English and American furnishings of the 17th and 18th centuries is immediately apparent.

Ayers' premium pieces reside in some of the finest homes and museums in America. Nationally renowned, Ayers is one of only five members, west of the Mississippi River, of the prestigious Art and Antique Dealers League of America, Inc.

Whether seeking a Chippendale secretary-desk, a Jacobean chest of drawers, or an important Georgian drum table (pictured), the quality you will find here is unsurpassed.

1298 South Broadway
722-3492

Hours: Mon.-Sat. 10-5:30
Sunday 12-5

Sometimes it is difficult to envision how a particular antique you have fallen in love with will appear in your home or office. At Antiques S'il Vous Plait, you can see Denver's finest traditional and formal furniture and unique accessories in beautiful, home-like vignettes. Against backgrounds of French wallpaper and oriental rugs, you will form a clear idea of how a piece will look in your setting, thus better appreciate the exquisite quality of these lovely articles.

Antiques S'il Vous Plait has furnished many of the offices in downtown Denver in quality executive furniture—for the company interested in the richness of traditional styling and the corporate investment facet of antiques.

Located in Denver's famed Antique Guild, Antiques S'il Vous Plait is owned by Leonard Lowery and Karen Utsler. Lowery, a nationally-known dealer in fine antiques, lived in Europe for many years and imported antiques throughout the country. Mrs. Utsler has performed commercial interior design. Her advice is invaluable to customers.

Together, they have accumulated a carefully selected treasure of European and American pieces—many from great American estates. Everything from music cabinets to four-poster beds may be found here; all imbued with that rich aura of time. They also have a varied collection of bibelot, china, and crystal. Everything at Antiques S'il Vous Plait is in top condition—much of it totally restored.

Antiques S'il Vous Plaît

Sloane Square

310 St. Paul
321-4277

**Mon.-Fri. 10 am-5 pm
Saturday 10 am-3 pm**

Sloane Square is for those who love authentic, fine antiques and who wish to live with what they collect.

Arranged comfortably in charming rooms in a converted Cherry Creek home are chair sets, Irish and Welch dressers, beautiful fireplace surrounds, desks for home and office, and other pieces richly grained in walnut, oak, mahogany, pine and fruitwood. Particu-larly appealing is the wide se-lection of coun-try tables—farm-house dining ta-bles, coffee tables, side tables, cricket ta-bles—just part of the shop's assortment of 18th and 19th centu-ry country French and English furniture.

Owner Dorothy Dabney has a keen eye for blending antique furniture with contemporary accessories, making the pieces both attractive and functional. Sloane Square period pieces are afforda-ble today . . . while timeless tomorrow.

PHOENIX

2368 15th Street
477-4411

Hours: Mon.-Sat. 11-6

In Egyptian mythology, the phoenix was a rare and beautiful bird that rose from its own ashes, a symbol of immortality. Like that mythical bird, the rare and unusual items at the Phoenix in downtown Denver have achieved their own enduring quality.

Earl Duncan, the well-traveled owner of this unusual establishment, has collected an extraordinary array of high-quality items ranging from objects d'art

to the fanciful. But it quickly becomes apparent, as you enter this beautiful, museum-quality gallery, that Earl Duncan's greatest passion is for hand-carved, wooden carousel animals.

The carousel was returned to Europe by the Medieval crusaders from Asia Minor, and it has been a Western fascination ever since. Among the many carousel items Duncan has procured is a 1915 American zebra made by the William Dentzel Co., a magnificent standing horse carved by the master carver, John Zalar, in 1910; an English roundabout ostrich, and many other fine carousel related items.

If carousels aren't your fancy there's plenty more in this plant-studded gallery to tempt the eye and the heart: collector-quality pre-Columbian art objects, rare vintage French wine, antique cameras, 17th century oils, Western art, fine weaponry, antique toys, and some Buffalo Bill Cody Wild West show souvenirs. Duncan also offers specialized interior design service so these rare items will fit comfortably into your home.

Whether you're a serious investor/collector or someone looking for the truly exceptional for your home, Phoenix will rise to the occasion.

Stuart-Buchanan

1235 S. Broadway
777-1136

Mon-Sat. 10 am-6 pm
And by appointment

Country living is full of easy grace and simple charms. "But city people can also enjoy this lifestyle," says Stuart Hough, who owns Stuart-Buchanan with his mother Carol and partner John Weber.

"We love country furniture and accessories," Hough says. "Clients who were looking for more formal furnishings have been quickly converted to the country style once they view our selection." With more than 12,000 square feet of display area on two floors, the Stuart-Buchanan Antique and Design Gallery can appeal to any taste.

"The simple style, function and grace of country furniture lends itself to both contemporary and antique interior design," Hough adds. "Even though we offer a simple design style, the most sophisticated collectors can find valuable pieces in our gallery."

Hough periodically makes trips to Europe to select antiques from England, France and other countries on the continent. These pieces often are shipped back to Denver in rough form, where craftspersons working with Stuart-Buchanan refinish and reupholster them. This in-house restoration service is available to all of the gallery's clients. The firm also offers appraisal and complete interior design services.

While Stuart-Buchanan specializes in antique American, French and English furniture, the showrooms also feature quilts, sporting and nature prints, folk art, such culinary items as French stoneware and brass and copper cooking ware, and even antique American office furniture. Recent additions to the collection include original lithographs by James Audubon and John Gould, and the most delightful (yet realistic) stoneware barnyard animals imaginable.

"We have always strived to increase the quality of our merchandise," Hough says. "We now feel that Stuart-Buchanan Antiques offers the finest collection of country furnishings available in the Rocky Mountain area."

Restaurants

Amidst the visual splendor of the Rockies and the frenetic pace of a booming energy capitol, Denver is sometimes overlooked as a great place to eat. In fact, its cuisine is excellent and very cosmopolitan, from Mexican enchiladas to Chinese moo-shi, from New York bagels to Moroccan couscous. Bon Appétit.

Denver is a city obsessed with greenery. Green lawns. Greenways. Green parks. ✻ Little wonder. The Mile High City was built on a dry, brown plain that averages a paltry 14 inches of precipitation a year. Denver became known early in its life as the "city of parks," trying to grow a verdant urban oasis on the edge of the "Great American Desert." ✻ In the 1980s, the city's parks are major reasons why Denver is a beautiful place to live. The city boasts more than 150 urban parks and 24 mountain parks, ranging in size from half an acre to 1,000 acres. Some of the parks are linked by greenways built along waterways and gulches. ✻ One of the larger, busier parks in the city is the 155-acre Washington Park. On any warm weekend afternoon the park is filled with joggers, sun worshippers, bicyclists, lawn bowlers, tennis players, and people watchers. Two lakes dot the park, providing enjoyment for fishermen and boaters. The park is well known for its extensive and lovely flower gardens. It is a historical park, too. The City Ditch, Denver's first irrigation canal and now a historical landmark, courses through the park, still supplying water to customers and feeding the lake at City Park. ✻ Denver began acquiring land for its parks well before the turn of the century. But the major impetus for improving and expanding the parks came from Denver's first powerful mayor, Robert Speer. Inspired by Europe's beautiful parks, Speer spent much of the century's first two decades beautifying Denver. Extensive irrigation and tree plantings were begun. Lakes such as those at Sloan's Lake and Washington Park were created. The mountain parks system, which includes Red Rocks, Genesee, and Summit Lake, was begun. ✻ Speer recognized Denver's hunger for greenery; he intuitively understood that as the city grew so did the people's desire to maintain that special sense of spaciousness so endemic to the West. Perhaps that's why one of Speer's first acts as mayor was to order the removal of all "Keep Off The Grass" signs.

Mon Petit

7000 W. 38th Ave.
424-4700

Hours: Mon.-Fri. 11:30 am-2:00 pm
Mon.-Sat. 6:00 pm-10:00 pm

Reservations required

"How do you describe a diamond?" says Frank Pourdad when talking of his Mon Petit restaurant. "If we are not number one, we are not number two."

Denver's gourmets who have visited Mon Petit heartily agree. Nearly all of them return again and again for its elegant decor and its superb French cuisine. How could you not return after the following scene?

Would monsieur like an appetizer for this evening? inquires the tuxedoed waiter politely.

You ponder over the escargots champignon, the pâté de fois gras de Strasbourg, the crêpe de crabe au Mon Petit.

For an *entrée*?

You glance again at the huge menu and realize that you could return to Mon Petit 42 times and never have to order the same entree. For lunch, there are a mere 24 choices.

There is roast rack of spring lamb, as only the French can prepare lamb. And the tournedos Bordelais with bone-marrow. And all those veal specialties and turbot veronique, frog's legs meunière, and quail.

And dessert, monsieur?

There's Méringue Mon Petit and Strawberries Cardinal and Mousse au Chocolat and . . . The wine list is even longer.

More than 100 choices, at prices from modest to a very expensive Chateau Lafitte Rothschild. Ah, but this meal is worth the grand gesture.

How can you resist the intimate plushness of Mon Petit, so like a miniature Versailles? There are private dining salons; and the mirror-draped walls echoing the candlelight and fresh flowers, the fourteenth-century European antiques, the expensive chandeliers. The polished corps of waiters moves soundlessly across the rich Persian carpets. During the summer you can even experience that wonderful European custom, dining *al fresco,* on Mon Petit's patio.

You finish your coffee and look around. Yes, Mon Petit. A diamond, indeed.

158 Fillmore
Cherry Creek North
355-6464

Lunch & Dinner Daily
Closed Sunday

When French cuisine was introduced to Vietnamese cooking a classic marriage was the result. That union was brought to Denver by Chez Thoa of Cherry Creek.

Chez Thoa introduces an elegant, sophisticated, yet friendly flavor to this nouvelle cuisine of the Orient. Diners can relax while savoring the culinary delights created by Thoa Fink, one of the owners of the restaurant.

If you have never eaten Vietnamese food, get ready for a wonderful dining adventure. One of Thoa's favorite dishes is Vit Quay—duck marinated for 48 hours, then slowly roasted and glazed, and served on a bed of rice noodles and lettuce.

Indulge in Bo Nhung Dam: thinly sliced beef cooked fondue style at your table, then wrapped in rice paper, rice noodles, mint garnish, and dipped in a delightful sauce. From the sea comes Tom Boc Thit: prawns embraced in a pate of shrimp, pork, black mushrooms, wrapped in rice paper and deep fried until crisp and golden brown. Accompanying the dish is a piquant sauce, Nuoc Mam.

Chez Thoa's continental side offers numerous French dishes. For example, Les Tournedos in a burgundy sauce topped with crab meat and asparagus spears, and also the classically prepared Salmon Papillon: fillets of salmon, covered with creamed spinach, wrapped in fillo leaves, baked to golden brown, served with a velvety sauce of curry.

Each entree comes with either soup or salad and sauteed vegetables of the evening. Tempting hors d'oeuvres include Cha Gio (Imperial Rolls), a mixture of chicken, pork, and mushrooms lightly crisped in rice paper, and the classic Vietnamese asparagus and crab soup, called "Mang Tay Nau," with fresh ground coffee or an espresso.

Phillip, the manager, and Mary Beth McGill, co-owner and hostess, keep the cosmopolitan Chez Thoa moving smoothly yet casually.

Full bar service is available, as well as a fine wine list including domestic and imported wines. Catering service is available for special occasions.

Bon Appetit and Chuc An Ngon Mieng.

Chez Thoa

THE COACH HOUSE RESTAURANT

10607 E. Dartmouth Ave.
751-5790

Hours: Mon.-Thurs. 6-10:30
 Fri.-Sat. 5:30-10:30
 Sunday 5:30-9
 Lunch 11:30-2, weekdays
Reservations accepted

Like a stroll through a quaint French countryside, dining at the Coach House is one of the more pleasurable experiences of life. Its nouvelle cuisine, its extensive wine list, its homey French charm renews the spirit as well as the palate.

The continental menu at the Coach House starts with an international appetizer tray second to none: crudite of seasonal vegetables, chicken liver pate, poached gulf shrimp, and assorted cheeses to whet the appetite. A mixed lettuce salad or soup comes next, along with the Coach House's homemade breads.

The entrees are prepared by a talented chef. The nouvelle cuisine includes French-style lamb chops broiled and served with mint sauce, veal St. Moritz, lemon duck, and steak au cinq poivres.

The fish and seafood dishes are especially good. Much of the seafood is flown in daily from the east and west coasts, with the menu including strawberry trout, emerald scallops, and giant scampi provencal. There are nightly surprises, too, from swordfish and lemon sole to salmon.

For dessert, select from an array of fresh cookies, pastries, meringues, and other sweets made by the House's own chefs.

The Coach House is proud of its extensive wine list, including many wines not available elsewhere in the Denver area. Try the wines not only at dinner but at the Coach House's exquisite lunch or during the 3 to 6 cocktail hour, with its complimentary — and incomparable — Coach House-prepared hors d'oeuvres.

All this is set in a charming atmosphere of leaded glass, warm fireplace, and overstuffed chairs. And if you want to create your own French countryside charm at home for friends, the Coach House now has its own catering service.

Chateau Pyrenees

6338 S. Yosemite Circle
770-6660

Every great city has a special restaurant synonymous with classic elegance. In Denver, that restaurant is the Chateau Pyrenees.

The exterior is reminiscent of a chateau in southern France with slit windows set into stone walls. The building seems incongruous against the backdrop of suburban southeast Denver, but inside there's a faraway sense of time and place.

The atmosphere within Chateau Pyrenees can only be described as magnificent. Soft lavender accents the decor, highlighted by an impressive crystal chandelier illuminating the two dining areas. These areas are divided by a raised platform and an ornate grand piano dating from 1874 and styled after Louis XVI, played expertly for listening and dancing. On the walls are original paintings by Marc Chagal and Frank Hopper. Polished waiters in tuxedos move smartly through the room, heightening the restaurant's special brand of sophistication.

Owned since 1980 by Austrian-born restaurateur Conrad Trinkaus, the cuisine has benefitted from his 25 years' experience at such fabled restaurants and hotels as George V and Plaza Athenee in Paris, various other first class restaurants in Europe, and the Four Seasons and Caesar's in New York. Trinkaus has expanded the old all-French menu to include many continental dishes, such as Dover Sole and Beef Wellington. The most popular dinner entrees are Medallions Pyrenees (medallions of beef tenderloin with wild mushrooms with a Burgundy wine sauce), Langoustine Thermidor (lobster), and such standards as Chateau Briand and rack of lamb—all produced with distinctive appeal to the most discriminating palate.

While expanding the menu, Trinkaus has been streamlining the restaurant's operation. "People no longer have to plan on spending the whole evening when they come here for dinner," he says. "My philosophy is that we will serve a delicious meal within the time required by the customer. This prompt service especially applies to luncheons."

Reservations are no longer absolutely necessary, he adds, but they are encouraged. Chateau Pyrenees is the only restaurant of its kind in the nation and reservations guarantee service.

"Where else can you dine in the atmosphere of a French chateau and have the elegance to enhance it?" Trinkaus asks.

His question is surely rhetorical.

THE FRESH FISH CO.
RESTAURANT & OYSTER BAR
MESQUITE WOOD BROILED FISH

**7800 E. Hampden Ave.
Fresh Fish Co. 740-9556
Knick's Saloon 740-9555**

You don't have to sniff the air to know that Denver is not the seafood capital of the world. But don't despair, seafood devotees. A fresh idea has come to town. The Fresh Fish Co. Restaurant and Oyster Bar.

Recently opened under the same roof as the already famous Knick's Saloon in Tiffany Plaza, The Fresh Fish Co. features Denver's only true oyster bar. Imagine: fresh shucked eastern oysters and clams, gulf shrimp cocktail, oysters Rockefeller, steamed clams.

And the fish! Fresh, boneless fish is flown in daily from both coasts. Standard fare includes Pacific red snapper, northern ling cod, salmon, Rocky Mountain trout, and such shellfish specialties as the shrimp skewer, sea scallop skewer, crab legs, lobster, and the finest New England clam chowder this side of Boston.

But watch especially for the chalkboard specials. Those are the surprise catches of the day. Shark, angler, swordfish, tuna—anything is possible, and probable. And all boneless fish is cooked with a distinctly Western touch: slowly broiled over mesquite wood while you watch. They don't have that in Boston. Or anywhere else in Denver, for that matter.

All dinners include sourdough bread, salad, coleslaw, and a choice of french fries, cottage cheese, new potatoes, or rice pilaf. If you bring a meat-and-potatoes friend there's New York strip steak for the evening menu. For lunch there's hamburger, chicken teriyaki, and luncheon steak. For your own seafood tastes there are Shrimp Louie and other classic seafood salads.

The Fresh Fish Co. carries on that great Sunday brunch tradition from Knick's: a buffet feast of fresh fruit, egg dishes, salads and a dessert table that will leave your taste buds throbbing.

And don't forget the adjacent Knick's. They're concentrating on what they know best: serving great drinks, offering disco and other music to dance to, and featuring some of the best promo nights in the city.

So if you can't always fly off to the coast for fresh seafood, visit The Fresh Fish Co. and Knick's Saloon. They're bringing the sea to the foot of the Rockies.

La Bola
900 Jersey
333-3888

La Bola Viva
6830 S. University Blvd.
771-4464

La Bola Grande
8000 E. Quincy
779-0191

La Bola Bravo
11602 W. 64th Ave.
423-5543

Phil Gonzales is a modest man who attributes the success of his La Bola restaurants to his employees. "I don't know," he says, "this thing just took off. I got lucky. I couldn't believe it."

Well . . . maybe so. Maybe it was luck. It was probably more like a lot of hard work.

The La Bola success story is grounded in a large amount of practical experience. After coming to Denver in 1959, Phil Gonzales was a cook for 10 years before he was offered a restaurant partnership. Later, he sold out and established the original La Bola at 900 Jersey Street. In time La Bola Bravo, La

Bola Grande, and La Bola Viva were opened. Collectively, they comprise, perhaps, the most popular Mexican food restaurants in the Denver area.

Luck? Maybe. But Phil hedges the bet by personally training each new cook, preferring to hire the inexperienced so he can teach them his own methods. Managers are personally taught every aspect of the business. Nothing is left to chance.

The proof of any restaurant is in the eating. Almost everybody in Denver has his own idea of what constitutes good Mexican food. It is, after all, a matter of taste. But the La Bola restaurants have earned awards from the Colorado Under-

ground Gourmet, Denver Magazine, the Nation's Restaurant News and others. Take their word for it—try a La Bola restaurant.

You might choose the popular La Bolallena, which translates colloquially as the "stuffed" Bola. It is a flour tortilla stuffed with cheese, tomatoes, onions, and other delightful surprises. Or you might try the Carne Asada, a thinly sliced cut of braised steak topped with green peppers, tomatoes, and an inimitable green chile.

La Bola restaurants are family oriented. Prices are moderate, from $2-$6. And by all means indulge in one of their excellent, huge, 27-ounce Margaritas.

La Bola restaurants—high quality at moderate price.

4609 E. Colfax
399-9282

Hours: Dinner Daily 6 pm-10 pm
Lunch Weekdays 11:30 am-2 pm
Reservations required

Mataam Fez

Ambience is an overrated claim at many restaurants. But at Mataam Fez ambience *is* an indispensable part of the cuisine. Chef-owner Abderafih Benjelloun has spared nothing to bring his native Morocco to East Colfax, from the authentic decor and traditional show-manship to the tangy cous-cous.

Eating Moroccan style is half the fun. Diners shed their shoes and lounge on cushions under a sprawling, bright-ly colored silk tent. And when Benjel-loun says dig in, he means it. Fin-gers only here, with huge towels pro-vided for cleaning. Waiters in caftans scurry to and fro, bringing relays of food until you want to beg them to stay away.

First comes *hari-ra,* a spicy mix of lamb and lentils, quickly followed by salads and *b'stilla,* Morocco's famous meat pie of layered chicken, eggs, lem-on, elusive herbs, and fragile pastry sprinkled with cin-namon and sugar.

If that isn't enough, there are a dozen entrees to choose from. Try the pot-roasted chicken with pickled lemons or the fiery lamb dish seasoned with apricots, or Cornish game hen in honey and herbs, or cous-cous, the native dish of Morocco.

This Moroccan feast goes on for hours. After all, in Morocco, says Chef Benjelloun, a meal is a ritual. You'll believe him after you watch the sharp-eyed waiters pour mint tea from pots held high over the diners' heads. They don't miss.

Whether you order the five-course or six-course dinner, you'll experience what few Americans find in dining—great food *and* great fun. Mataam Fez also has an excellent wine list featuring Moroccan wines and a cozy lounge.

One final note. Chef Benjelloun is justifiably proud of his creations, and he emphasizes that they are Moroccan, not Middle Eastern dishes. The very best Moroccan. Mataam Fez is con-sidered one of the finest Moroccan restaurants in the United States.

THE BROKER RESTAURANTS

For the Broker nearest you, call 893-5065

Hours: Lunch, Mon.-Fri. 11 am-3 pm
Dinner, Mon.-Sat. 5 pm-11 pm
Sundays 5 pm-10 pm

If you've ever felt like robbing a bank, The Broker Restaurant seems to give you that opportunity. Almost everyone who has ever dined there has felt that he's getting away with something after encountering The Broker's unlimited appetizer bowl of shrimp.

Overindulging your taste for shrimp, however, is a mistake; you really must leave room to enjoy the other delights on The Broker's fine menu: the Trout Almondine; Beef Wellington; Filet and Lobster. Whatever your taste, The Broker is sure to have something to delight your palate.

More than a restaurant, The Broker is a landmark, located in the basement of the old Denver National Bank Building in the heart of Seventeenth Street. The vault, where millions of dollars once reposed, remains intact, complete with gleaming multi-ton door and polished cage-like steel bars.

If your preference is gracious, intimate dining, The Broker provides warm, plushly appointed little nooks for two.

Having dinner with a large party? No problem. Another large dining room opposite the vault gives you plenty of room for any size group. The Broker even has a library for bookworms who like to read as they dine. Feel free to browse. You'll find everything from Aristotle to Zola.

The Broker is a fine restaurant without being stuffy or pretentious. Relax. Have a good time. Enjoy a cocktail from the lounge, or select a choice wine from the well-stocked cellar. By all means absorb and bask in the diverse atmosphere of The Broker, but never forget that it is the excellent menu that keeps people coming back.

Other fine Broker restaurants are: The Wellington Broker, The Country Broker, The Denim Broker, The Buckingham Broker, and the Boulder Broker Inn. As the names imply, each provides its own atmosphere for your dining pleasure.

bombay club

1128 Grant Street
837-1571

Hours:
    Lunch Mon.-Fri. 11:30 a.m.-2:30 p.m.
    Dinner Sun.-Thu. 5:30 p.m.-9:30 p.m.
        Fri.-Sat. 5:30 p.m.-10:30 p.m.
Reservations for 6 or more

If you don't believe the smooth, sophisticated sounds of American jazz blend magically with the spicy, exotic flavors of Indian, Middle Eastern, and West African dishes, you haven't visited the Bombay Club.

Owner Michael Vernon has brought a "new international flavor of service, food, and amenities" to Denver eating. While riffs of some of the best live jazz in town drift down from the upstairs cabaret, diners plunge into gastronomic experiences that would make John Coltrane wail on his sax all night long.

Once you're settled in the relaxing Victorian dining room, begin with a hearty lentil soup seasoned with butter and garlic, or a vegetable curry soup delicately touched with ginger. Follow it with a Moroccan-style salad of carrots, raisins, and walnuts, or a tabouleh salad made with spiced, cracked wheat.

Deciding what comes next gets tougher. The specialty of the Bombay Club is the classic North Indian Tandoori barbecue. Whether lamb, beef, or chicken, the meats linger in lime juice, then in a red spice paste before being gently seared and accompanied by chutneys and rice.

Among the other enticing entrees are plump Indonesian lamb chops marinated in soy sauce and fresh green ginger; a West African stew of black beans, rice, and shrimp; and fresh fish baked with coriander and garlic. The menu also features a curried "Brahmin Feast" from India, those delectable falafels from Egypt, and Moroccan salad made with chicken, apples, and walnuts. If that's not enough, chef Lorraine is always coming up with something new.

While there is an ample selection of beverages, one recommendation, especially for the spicier dishes, is something from the long list of imported beers or reasonably priced wine list.

And nothing accents one of these spicy meals better than a slice of sweet apricot rum cake, a creamy Cuban flan flavored with pineapple, or a meringue and cream fantasy called Floating Jamaica. They are made for Scheherazade.

THE FORT

**Junction US 285 and Highway Colo. 8
south of Morrison
697-4771**

**Hours: Mon.-Thurs. 6 pm-9:30 pm
Fri.-Sat. 6 pm-10 pm
Sunday 5 pm-9 pm
Reservations are suggested**

Bent's Old Fort on the Arkansas River, built in 1833, became legendary as a fur-trading headquarters and stopover for men like Kit Carson and Jim Bridger.

The Fort Restaurant, built in 1962, is an authentic 3/4 scale replica of Bent's Old Fort, and has become something of a legend in its own time as the headquarters for superb dining.

Nestled in the foothills, the adobe-constructed fort captures that old rawhide-n-black-powder setting with a courtyard campfire and a commanding view of Denver.

Diners can sample authentic early Western fare in cozy comfort, surrounded by Western and Indian art, and roaring fires. They can choose from a wide variety of seafoods and Colorado beef steaks cooked over real charcoal.

For appetizers, try Oysters Roberto, buffalo sausage, or Rocky Mountain oysters. Entrees include fresh swordfish and salmon, Gonzales steak stuffed with mild or hot chiles, prime rib, broiled trout, lobster tail, and corn fed buffalo meat.

All entrees are accompanied by cheese tostadas, delicious Fort-baked breads, salad, potato, and fresh vegetables. For desserts, diners can savor cheesecake, a rum and chocolate concoction called Negrita, or prairie cake—a rich butter crumb cake that improves upon an old West standard.

Naturally, there's a fantastic bar. Among the most popular drinks are the Hailstorm (an historic spirit served in a pint Mason jar). There's the classic margarita, and the Chimaja whiskey (a mountain herb-flavored bourbon popular in Old West bars). The Fort Restaurant also offers a wide selection of outstanding wines.

The Fort Restaurant, where the romance of the Colorado Territory meets the sophistication of the 1980s, is located 25 minutes southwest of downtown Denver.

Gasho of Japan

Because dining was never meant to be dull.

Prudential Plaza
1627 Curtis Street
892-5625
Lunch Mon.-Sat. 11:30 a.m.-2:30 p.m.
Dinner Mon.-Thurs. 5 p.m.-10 p.m.
Dinner Fri.-Sat. 5 p.m.-11 p.m.
Sunday dinner 4 p.m.-9 p.m.

Denver Technological Center
I-25 and East Belleview
773-3277
Lunch Mon.-Sat. 11:30 a.m.-2 p.m.
Dinner Sun.-Thurs. 5 p.m.-10 p.m.
Dinner Fri.-Sat. 5 p.m.-11 p.m.
Sunday brunch 10 a.m.-2 p.m.

Close your eyes. Let your imagination run wild. You're among characters from the novel "Shogun" with its Samurai warriors leaping and their gleaming steel blades slashing. Then enjoy lunch or dinner at one of Denver's. two fine Gasho of Japan restaurants.

The two experiences share striking similarities. But rather than a Samurai warrior, a Japanese chef in white jacket, black slacks and blue hat with matching scarf, stands before you. "Kon-nichi-wa— welcome," he says, bowing.

He quickly arranges your meal on the hibachi grill. Tender prime beef. Plump shrimp. Scallops. Lobster. Chicken. Or whatever you've chosen for an entree. Vegetables include zucchini, mushrooms, bean sprouts, onions and rice.

Now, in an amazing display of speed and grace, knives flash, cutting vegetables into bite-size pieces. You dig in with chopsticks, dipping a morsel into sweet mustard or ginger sauce provided for additional spice.

There are two Gasho of Japan restaurants in Denver, each open for lunch and dinner. The Denver Technological Center Gasho is modeled after 400-year-old Gasho farmhouses still found in Japan. Sunday brunch is also popular here. Downtown the Gasho in the Prudential Plaza building offers a similar setting and one of the most unique cocktail lounges in the area with a beautiful, handcrafted teahouse.

For those seeking adventure in dining and outstanding cuisine, try Gasho of Japan—where dining was never meant to be dull!

EMIL'LENE'S SIRLOIN HOUSE

16000 Smith Rd.
366-6674

Mon. - Sat. 11:30 a.m. - 2:00 p.m.
**   5:30 p.m. - 11:00 p.m.**
Sunday   5-10 p.m.

Don't panic if a friend offers to take you for a ride, then drives into the prairie east of Denver. See all the cars parked around that rustic old farm house? Smell the aroma in the air? Relax. Get ready for a truly fine eating experience.

Frills, gimmicks, and plush atmosphere abound throughout Denver, but few restaurants duplicate what Emil-Lene's Sirloin House is renowned for since 1959—the finest of prime beef, charcoal broiled to perfection.

No need for a menu at the Sirloin House. Although they offer a daily special other than steak, you won't want to forego the pleasure of something like New York Strip Steak: 16 ounces of tender, succulent sirloin, served with salad and baked potato or french fries. Naturally the Sirloin House offers other cuts of beef. If you have room, dessert is taste-tingling homemade ice cream.

Reservations are recommended at the Sirloin House. Prices range from $8-$16. Bar? Yup. Atmosphere??? Now where else can you sit under a cottonwood tree in one of the dining rooms?

bagel nosh®

All right, reader, pay close attention to the following. You'll be quizzed at the end.

    ba•gel (ba'gel) n. Yiddish. A donut-shaped roll of yeast dough boiled in water and baked. Delicious.
    nosh (nosh) n. Yiddish. 1. A snack or treat. —v.2. to snack.
    Bagel Nosh n. 1. A highly successful, innovative restaurant. —vi. 2. To savor any of 10 delicious bagel flavors, from plain to pumpernickel. Preferably with friends.

    Educating Coloradans about the joys of eating bagels has been one of the larger tasks of Bagel Nosh owners Barbara and Bernie Cohen. That they've admirably succeeded is evident by the fact they've expanded to a fourth deli in only five years, and have plans for more soon.

    With all those authentic, New York-style delicatessen specialties, though, the task of educating never ends. There are knishes (a potato or meat mixture wrapped in puff pastry, served hot), kugel (noodle pudding), lox (smoked salmon, salty), and nova (not salty). Bagel Nosh also serves fresh cheeses and meats, chopped liver, and several flavors of homemade cheesecake.

    Traditionally, bagels are served with lox and cream cheese (Bagel Nosh has several incredible varieties). But the Cohens have developed the "pizza bagel" topped with tomato sauce, two cheeses, and heated. Or you can pile on roast beef, turkey breast, salami, liverwurst, pastrami, and other items. Be creative. Mix your own.

    Bagels also are served with hot homemade soups, salads, barbecued chicken, draft beer, and other specials on the Nosh's breakfast, lunch, and dinner menus. If you don't wish to eat knish-to-knish with everyone, take out your order. Better yet, have Bagel Nosh deliver. Their catering service can handle five people or 500. Order their Kettle of Fish special or their Big Wheel, a one-foot-around bagel stuffed with corned beef, roast beef, turkey, and several delicious cheeses.

    Of course, learning what's what, which to choose, and how to pronounce it comes best with repeated on-site visits to Bagel Nosh. Can you think of a better learning experience?

Wuthering Heights

7785 West Colfax
238-7774

Hours: Mon.-Sat. from 5 p.m.
Sun. from 4 p.m.

Just as Emily Bronte's *Wuthering Heights* has become a classic among novels, Wuthering Heights on west Colfax has become a classic among Denver restaurants.

Step inside this English manor and you step back in time. It is an unhurried time, a time when dining was a pleasure to be shared leisurely with friends and family. Everything about Wuthering Heights enhances that mood, from its muted lighting and lush overstuffed furniture to its antiques and French-

Moroccan tapestries. At Wuthering Heights a fireplace can be seen from every table.

Begin the evening with a before-dinner drink in the stained-glass lounge, as comfortable as Heathcliff's drawing room. Then onto dinner. There are 23 full dinners at Wuthering Heights, including prime rib, lobster tail, Beef Wellington, crab legs and Teriyaki Chicken, and Heathcliff's pork chop with baked apple.

Appetizers range from escargots to marinated herring. And every meal comes with English-style oxtail soup, salad plate, potato, vegetable, fruit sherbet with the entree, and Wuthering Heights' special breads. Dinner includes a sundae or a cordial such as coffee

brandy or peppermint schnapps. It is a meal fit for an English king.

But don't get the impression that Wuthering Heights is stuffy. Dress casually if you like. Come to relax and enjoy the soft background music. Bring the children. In fact, Wuthering Heights features children's specials every night. Just ask your waiter.

Speaking of waiters, most of them have worked at Wuthering Heights since it opened in 1976. Clearly they enjoy the restaurant as much as the diners who return time after time.

So if you are in the mood for unhurried, delicious dining, visit Wuthering Heights. Step back to a time when dining was what it was always meant to be.

DRAGON PALACE

5071-A S. Syracuse St.
I-25 and Belleview
779-9022

Hours: Mon.-Thurs. 11 am-10:30 pm
       Fri.-Sat. 11 am-11 pm
       Cocktail hours, weekdays 2:30-6
       Sunday brunch 11 am-2:30 pm
       Sunday dinner 5 pm-10:30 pm
Reservations required

If you've developed a jaded appetite for the typical Cantonese style of Chinese cooking, prepare for a renewal. Get ready for the superb Szechuan and Mandarin cuisine of the Dragon Palace.

Nothing at this authentic Chinese restaurant is routine; not its decor, not its service, especially not its food. The Dragon Palace is owned and operated by Jim Chang of the former Golden Dragon, who brought Szechuan and Mandarin cooking to Denver in 1973 and was promptly honored by Esquire Magazine as one of the 100 best new restaurants in the country.

It's easy to taste why. Most Mandarin and Szechuan dishes are sauteed, accompanied by a brown spicy red hot sauce. Spring rolls, scallion pancakes, hot and sour soup, and steamed rice with pork and pickle soup are just some of the appetizers and soups to get you off to a sound beginning.

Among the entrees is a house specialty, the classic Moo-shi pork (beef, shrimp, or chicken as you prefer), spicy hot diced chicken, crisp Chunking duck seasoned with oriental sauce and fried golden crisp, or the sizzling Kou-Bar consisting of shrimp and assorted diced meat sauteed with vegetables and simmered in a blended Mandarin sauce.

All this is followed by such unconventional desserts as sweet red bean pastry or honeyed crisp banana.

The Dragon Palace is like a visit to the Far East. In fact, owner Jimmy Chang made three trips to China to order the furnishings; and the authenticity is self-evident in hand-carved wood artifacts, the baked tile roof, and Chinese wall hangings.

A Chinese brunch is served Saturday and Sunday, and private banquet facilities are available. The Dragon Palace also features a happy hour Monday through Friday. After sampling such complimentary appetizers as Drunk Chicken and spring rolls, you'll know that staying for dinner is the only sensible thing to do.

Hotels

As a major host and tourist city, Denver has long prided itself on the quality of its first-rate hotels, both in their comfort and their facilities. There's nothing frontier about these accommodations.

If Denver is the gateway to the Rocky Mountains, then Stapleton International Airport is surely the gateway to Denver. ⅂ *Served by 23 scheduled airlines, Stapleton is the sixth busiest airport in the nation, with direct flights to Canada, Mexico, and Europe. More than 1,300 daily landings and departures carry snowbirds toting skis, vacationers outfitted in new cowboy hats, and oil executives lugging heavy briefcases.* ⅂ *Perhaps more than any single public or private enterprise, Stapleton, aided by the smaller airports of Arapahoe and Jefferson counties, has dramatically helped to transform Denver from a sleepy regional capital to a major American city. In the past decade alone the number of passengers arriving and departing Stapleton has increased 300 percent.* ⅂ *Denver stakes its claim as a major regional transportation and distribution hub at Stapleton International Airport. Stapleton has few delays due to weather. It is one of the most accessible airports in the nation (only seven miles east of downtown), a principal factor in the decision of many major corporations to locate their headquarters in Denver.* ⅂ *It wasn't always so. When Stapleton Field, as it was first known, was dedicated in 1929 it consisted of four graveled runways, a hanger and a small terminal. Critics ridiculed it as "Stapleton's Folly," as it was Mayor Benjamin Stapleton who had pushed for its creation.* ⅂ *Today, the original 640 acres of sagebrush "out in the country" has become 4,679 acres of prime real estate surrounded by a huge metropolitan area. And the need for a larger airport grows daily as aviation demands increase.* ⅂ *Stapleton's Folly has become a gateway of vision.*

1701 California
825-1300
For reservations call toll free
1/800-228-9290

In the dramatic growth of downtown Denver, a spectacular new hotel has emerged . . . the Denver Marriott Hotel-City Center.

Located in the heart of the Queen City, this beautiful 612 room deluxe hotel offers luxurious accommodations for conventions, fine restaurants, and exceptional service for both the business traveler and the casual visitor.

Guest rooms at the Marriott Hotel-City Center are especially luxurious, including 29 Parlor Suites, 12 Executive Suites, and two Presidential Suites. Special VIP service is available on the Concierge levels with continental breakfast served daily, full time personal service, and major national newspapers delivered to the door.

Visitors will discover several exciting restaurants under the Marriott roof, beginning with gourmet dining in the contemporary southwestern splendor of Mattie Silks'. Antique furniture, brass, warm woods, and lush greenery strike the note at Marjolaines, serving breakfast, lunch, and dinner. And don't miss The Gallery, a lobby bar overlooking City Center Plaza. Another restaurant and lounge, Charms, serves not only luncheon specialties, but provides piano music every night for a romantic atmosphere.

Especially designed for conventions, the Marriott Hotel-City Center houses the largest ballroom in downtown Denver. The Colorado Ballroom offers 14,500 square feet of unobstructed space, and accommodates up to 2,100 people for meetings and 1,500 for banquets. Separated from the Colorado Ballroom by a sizable convention lobby, the Denver Ballroom provides space for 900. Rooms for smaller conferences and board meetings also are available.

In addition, the Marriott Hotel-City Center has an indoor pool, hydrotherapy pool, saunas, gift shop, game room, airline and travel information desk, and car rental service.

Plan your next convention, meeting, or trip at the Denver Marriott Hotel-City Center. A great hotel growing with a great city.

**1750 Welton St.
571-1200**

The Fairmont Hotel, one of Denver's newest luxury hotels, provides a fine setting for meetings, conventions or overnight visits. Like its sisters in San Francisco, Dallas and New Orleans, the hotel's service and decor are intended to make each guest feel at home.

The 26-story hotel boasts two ballrooms and 11 meeting rooms, all singularly decorated. Each room is equipped to provide the utmost in comfort to organizations holding a convention at the hotel, whether for 30 or 3,000. The 550 guest rooms and 26 suites are spaciously and singularly decorated. No two are alike.

There are two restaurants in the hotel, in addition to 24-hour room service and a lobby Cocktail Terrace. The Marquis — a most distinguished Denver restaurant and winner of the *Travel/Holiday* Fine Dining Award— offers gourmet dining amid an intimate setting and easy listening in its lounge. McGuire's, a 'round the clock specialty restaurant, reflects Denver's easy informality and friendliness. Additionally, the Moulin Rouge features an extraordinary brunch on Sunday and holidays.

The staff at the Fairmont Hotel echoes Denver's outgoing and courteous atmosphere. Proud of their two-year-old hotel, they are eager to acquaint the visitor with it and all that Denver offers.

The Sky Court, an outdoor recreational complex located on the fourth floor, is available to each Fairmont guest. Sun, exercise or relaxation are offered via a heated swimming pool, tennis court and a ⅛ mile running track.

Denver's Fairmont Hotel offers visitors a home-away-from-home designed to enhance meetings, conventions or leisure travel.

THE Brown Palace HOTEL

321 17th Street
825-3111

The Brown Palace.

The hotel "where the world registers."

A legacy of elegance, service, incomparable dining. Denver's most famous—and still its finest—hotel.

A hotel that grew up with Denver. A place where Buffalo Bill once roamed. Kings and queens. The Summer White House for President Eisenhower, and host to nearly every president since Teddy Roosevelt.

Built in 1892 from red granite and Arizona sandstone, the 10-story Brown Palace has since added a 22-story adjoining tower and expanded its accommodations to 480 individualized guest rooms to please the most world-wise traveler.

Along with its luxurious guest rooms, "The Brown" features an in-house florist, drug store, beauty and barber shops, dress shop, art gallery, and two airline ticket agencies.

Yet the Brown has managed to retain its Victorian heritage. The striking atrium lobby, with its Mexican onyx paneling and stained glass, still awes. And what hotel today boasts its own carpentry, finishing, and upholstery shops so as to insure that repairs and changes maintain the original integrity?

Conveniently located in the heart of Denver's downtown financial, shopping, and cultural districts, the Brown is ideal for conventions and meetings. Meeting rooms, equipped with audio-visual facilities, include a beautiful Grand Ballroom employing a movable stage complete with theater lighting.

The Brown's dining is world renowned. The San Marco Room has been a Denver tradition for more than 30 years,with its Brown Palace Orchestra and strolling San Marco Strings. The Palace Arms offers award-winning continental cuisine, and the Ship Tavern is famous both for its food and its Old World charm. And all of the hotel's baked goods are prepared fresh in-house.

The Brown Palace.

A hotel that still cares about the greatness it was born with.

REGENCY

3900 Elati
(I-25 & 38th)
458-0808

A great hotel is more than a building full of guest rooms. One doesn't come to town just to sleep. Spacious meeting facilities, varied dining and entertainment, recreational facilities, personal service, style, and those subtle but all-important extras are the mark of any great hotel. Such is The Regency in Denver.

The meeting facilities alone make The Regency one of the most sought-after hotels along the Front Range. A total of 63,000 square feet is available for exhibits, banquets, large or small meetings and gatherings.

One of Colorado's largest ballrooms, seating 2,500 auditorium-style, is located at The Regency. The Palladium Theater seats 212 comfortably for lectures or audio-visual shows (equipment available). And the hotel's 30 rooms designated for meetings include smaller, more intimate facilities.

Whether a major convention or a small business conference, The Regency can cater any meal requirements, including banquet dinners for up to 3,900 people at a time.

For more intimate or casual dining, The Regency offers several fine restaurants and lounges. If you're hungry for delicious continental cuisine amidst elegant surroundings, visit Jake's. And for an exciting night of dancing and fun, try Shenanigans Dance Club.

In the mood for cocktails and quiet conversation? Drop in to the Stuff'd Shirt with its relaxing piano bar. The London Grill also offers casual dining from 6:30 a.m. to midnight, and the coffee shop is open for breakfast and lunch. Whatever your culinary desires and needs, The Regency has it.

If you're looking for some strenuous exercise, visit The Regency's indoor and outdoor swimming pools or the tennis courts. There's an exercise room with the latest in weight and conditioning equipment. A stay at The Regency also provides access to a golf course and membership into an expansive indoor health and racquetball club. And when you've had your share of exercise, relax in The Regency's sauna.

The subtle extras are often what bring guests back to a hotel. The Regency provides free limousine service to and from the airport, and to and from downtown Denver. There are acres of free parking. And the staff—what can one say about The Regency's outstanding special Western hospitality and personal service? You have to experience it to believe it.

Of course, all the meeting facilities, fine dining, and recreational features don't overshadow the heart of the hotel—the sumptuous accommodations. The Regency has 415 superbly appointed suites and guest rooms with service at the touch of a button.

When you come to visit Denver and the Rockies, The Regency is your gateway. Conveniently located near I-25 and I-70, the hotel is only half an hour from the mountains and 1 hour from major ski resorts. Downtown business, shopping and night life is just minutes away, as are the sporting arenas which host major league hockey, football, basketball, and indoor soccer.

Whatever your needs—a suite for two or a convention hall for 2,000—The Regency has it all.

THE DENVER HILTON

1550 Court Place
893-3333

The Denver Hilton, located in downtown Denver, opened in April of 1960 and since then has continued the well known Hilton tradition of fine service, excellent meeting and banquet facilities, and comfortable accommodations.

The Denver Hilton is a full service hotel offering a wide array of convention facilities. The hotel's ballrooms, meeting rooms and exhibit areas offer some of the most versatile convention planning and banquet needs in the Rocky Mountain area. As a convention center, the Denver Hilton cannot be matched. The hotel's efficient professional meeting staff can turn a gathering into an occasion to remember. With the flexible type of function and banquet space, the hotel is capable of handling groups from 10 to 2100 people.

The Denver Hilton is proud to have three great restaurants, which offer the finest in cuisine: Trader Vic's, The Beef Baron, and The Wicker Works Restaurant and Lounge. Feast on delicacies from Trader Vic's famous Chinese Ovens or enjoy traditional American Cuisine served in the romantic South Seas atmosphere. Be sure to try an exotic rum concoction prepared in the Mai Tai Lounge. For lunch Monday through Friday, try the Beef Baron Restaurant known for its famed Colorado beef and its variety of dishes served throughout lunch. For more casual dining, The Wicker Works, a garden-like atmosphere, is just right for the breakfast, lunch or dinner encounter. Order a la carte or take advantage of the quick service offered at the delectable salad bar and buffet. A few other popular locations in the hotel are The Pub, a favorite retreat for a cocktail or Molly's Ice Cream Emporium, to indulge in a single scoop or a Mile High creation — everything from syrup to nuts!

Within minutes of the hotel are many of the city's major tourist attractions, including the Denver Center for the Performing Arts, the Denver U.S. Mint, the Denver Art Museum, the Museum of Natural History, the Botanical Gardens, and the Denver Zoo.

Whether it be professional assistance in planning a meeting, convention, or banquet, The Denver Hilton awaits you.

4900 DTC Parkway
779-1100

The Sheraton Denver Tech Center is a five-story, 319-room hotel located in the prestigious Denver Technological Center, a planned business community in southeast Denver.

From the moment you step into the atrium lobby, with its tree-lined courtyard and cobblestone walks, you'll become part of a tradition that separates the exceptional from the ordinary. The exceptional begins with the Sheraton's unique amenities: Cafe in the Park; the "Fifth Avenue," with service and specialty shops; a 24-hour New York-style Delicatessen; the Gazebo lounge; Lilly's contemporary nightclub, and a complete indoor sports complex with tennis and racquetball.

The Sheraton Denver Tech Center welcomes you to rooms that reflect a commitment to luxurious comfort. Each has a remote-control color TV, digital clock radio, sitting area and refrigerator. For the discerning traveler, The Summit, a special executive wing, offers supreme accommodations in a private club atmosphere. Your concierge will see to your every need, from a personal greeting to arranging your travel schedule. Specialized amenities include complimentary breakfast with newspaper, cocktails and hors d'oeuvres, beverage-stocked refrigerator and toiletries.

The hotel also features complete convention facilities, a full service conference center with theatre, and a 12,000 square foot exhibition hall.

Sheraton Denver Tech Center

The Cosmo
UPTOWN

1780 Broadway
861-9000

Convenience is everything to the businessman on the go, and the Plaza Cosmopolitan Hotel is close to the heart of everything in Denver.

Stapleton International Airport is only 20 minutes away. Within easy walking distance is the financial center of the Rocky Mountains, great shopping and historical sites, and entertainment. Some of the best entertainment, as a matter of fact, is right in the Cosmo itself with Thursday tea dances, Saturday Big Band dances, and Sunday jazz jams.

Also in the hotel is great eating and roomy, versatile meeting facilities. Eleven meeting and banquet rooms accommodate from 7 to 1,500 people. Sound and audio equipment, telephones, and support services also are available.

Dining is exceptional, with Don the Beachcomber's famous Polynesian and American cuisine. Luncheon specials and lively evening entertainment highlight the Off Broadway Lounge. And the Broadway Deli is a must for visitors and locals alike.

As you would expect from one of Denver's oldest and best-loved hotels, the 400 guest rooms at the Plaza Cosmopolitan are spacious and beautifully appointed. For a dimension beyond elegance the Cosmo extends the luxuries and amenities of its Plaza Level, including complimentary limousine service, engraved stationery, concierge service, continental breakfast, and the exclusive Derrick Club lounge.

Another bonus for the businessman is the Preferred Corporate Account. With this membership card you will receive guaranteed room rates, express check-in, complimentary continental breakfast, check cashing privileges, and a host of other special services.

Every guest at the Plaza Cosmopolitan has the convenience of the hotel's newsstand, valet services, men's and women's clothing shops, and an art gallery. And of course there is always the warm, Western hospitality shown by a Cosmo staff whose main objective is to serve you.

RAMADA RENAISSANCE

MANAGED BY HOSPITALITY SYSTEMS, INC.

**3200 S. Parker Rd.
695-1700**

For Denver, the opening of the spectacular Ramada Renaissance Hotel in the southeast metro area has established a new concept in "haute hotel": a luxury hotel in a resort setting.

This brand new hotel combines European hospitality with the finest American contemporary comforts, in one of the most fire-safe buildings in the country. Personal, concierge treatment is the rule, with decorator-designed rooms, king-size beds, and quality toiletries.

One of the most appealing touches of this hotel is its resort setting. Guests have privileges at the nearby Meadow Hills Country Club as well as boating access to the Cherry Creek Reservoir, which can be seen from many of the guest rooms.

The International Athletic Club adjoining the hotel also provides guest privileges. You can indulge in its racquetball courts, Olympic size pool, Nautilus fitness center, running track, complete gym, saunas, sun room and steam room. The hotel itself contains a heated swimming pool.

The Renaissance offers two restaurants: Don the Beachcomber, with exotic Polynesian and continental cuisine and cocktails, and Summerfield's International Market, which features lighter fare with lines of sandwiches and savory soups.

Caper's is the hotel's night spot, jumping with live contemporary music. For a quiet drink, there is the lobby bar. And soon to open will be a second bar and an exclusive gourmet-style French restaurant.

The Renaissance is perfect for meetings and conferences, offering 16,000 square feet of meeting space with nine meeting rooms, including the state's third-largest ballroom.

With the completion of 299 elegantly appointed rooms, the Ramada Renaissance is building an additional 200 rooms, scheduled for completion in the fall of 1982. The hotel is the premiere facility of the new luxurious Ramada Renaissance hotels around the world.

Exclusive Transportation

The jet and the automobile transformed Denver from a sleepy regional capitol to a major metropolitan city. Whether you need to fly or drive, consult our listings for the finest in exclusive transportation.

Anchoring the northwest end of Denver's famed 17th Street is a stately yet forlorn-looking structure: Union Station. A few passengers from Amtrak and the Rio Grande Railroad trickle in daily. But most of the time Union Station is a quiet place where one's footsteps echo inside its cavernous interior. ⅃ Yet Union Station once greeted America. Under its portals, and for a while through the famed "Welcome" arch, surged the masses of visitors, job seekers, businessmen, and health seekers ("lungers," the locals called them) who would change Denver forever. ⅃ The grand Union Station almost never had its chance to play Denver's ambassador. In the 1860s, despite the promising rush of gold seekers in 1859-60, Denver was stagnating. By 1870, in fact, Denver's official population of 4,759 had increased by only 10 souls in ten years. Compounding the inertia was the fact the transcontinental railroad had bypassed Denver in favor of Cheyenne 106 miles to the north. Denver's future looked bleak. ⅃ Fortunately, some of Denver's most powerful leaders took matters into their own hands. John Evans, the territorial governor, along with such bankers as Jerome B. Chaffee and David Moffat, formed the Denver Pacific Railway and built a line to Cheyenne. Soon half a dozen rail lines converged on Denver, bringing in the wealth from the Rockies and the champagne and people from the East. Between 1870 and 1880 Denver's population exploded 700 percent. She never looked back. ⅃ The first Union Station was built in 1881 to consolidate a proliferation of depots and to handle the thousands of people moving to Denver in the late 19th century. The station was rebuilt in 1894 following a fire, and the present structure was erected in 1912. The rise of the automobile and the jet airplane after World War II, when Denver experienced its latest—and still continuing—boom, made the railroads and Union Station nearly obsolete. ⅃ Down the street the skyscrapers have mushroomed. Office workers and shoppers scurry to and fro, oblivious to the existence, or historical importance, of Union Station. Only the echoes of footsteps feebly mimic its glorious past.

AERO EXECUTIVE

CHARTER SERVICE

JETWINDS AVIATION

3095 S. Parker Rd., #110
Aurora
696-1771

Imagine . . .

No more waiting in lines at airports. No more annoying baggage claims hassles. Freedom from delays of scheduled flights.

Call Jetwinds Aviation and write your own airline ticket.

Available 24 hours a day—and ready to fly in one hour—Jetwinds' FAA-certified pilots can depart from either Stapleton International or Arapahoe County Airports.

Jetwinds can get you to destinations where the airlines can't go, saving valuable time and leaving you fresher for your important business appointments.

Jetwinds will get you there in the comfort and class you deserve. Sit back in plush leather seats. Listen to stereo music, enjoy hot or cold food and beverage service. Hold in-flight conferences. Jetwinds can arrange such ground amenities as limousine service and hotel accommodations.

If you need important documents delivered anywhere in the United States, Jetwinds will meet your deadline. Their high-speed, over the weather flying pressurized Learjets are ideal as

air ambulances. And Jetwinds is FAA-certified to fly worldwide if you need to travel to Europe or South America.

Jetwinds is also a good operating partner for companies or individuals wanting to own an aircraft without the expense and headaches of a full-time flight operation. Jetwinds can help better utilize the aircraft, reduce operational costs, perform maintenance, and provide ready crews.

High standards for flight crews and maintenance is paramount at Jetwinds. Their pilots have extensive experience in Learjets and other aircraft, and are "Flight Safety International"-trained, airline-rated professionals.

Mausolf
CLASSIC CARS
OF DENVER

4651 S. Broadway

**Phone 761-4680
Saturdays, Sundays & Evenings**

Mausolf Classic Cars had a very modest beginning. "I was 14 when I bought my first car," says Ken Mausolf. "It was a Model T that didn't run. I made it run and sold it for twice what I paid for it." By age 16, Ken owned six cars. Their total value was only $200, but the car collecting bug had become deeply ingrained.

Raised on a farm in Kansas, Ken decided early that there were easier ways to make a living. Eventually, he became an interior designer, moved to Denver, and met his wife Eileen, also a designer, who shared his love for collecting old cars.

Still active interior designers, Ken and Eileen also own a public relations firm, and a diamond and gold investment business. But, indisputably, their great love is cars. In addition to Mausolf Classic Cars, they run a limousine rental service, Royalty Rental Limousine, Ltd. and a classic car investment firm. So deep is that affection that Eileen even has a name for each Rolls-Royce in their collection—Pegasus, McBeth, Gwenevere, Charles, Victoria; the list goes on and on. There is no question that Ken and Eileen own one of the largest collections of classic and unique automobiles in the world. A far cry from the first Model T.

Obviously Mausolf Classic Cars is not your usual South Broadway used car dealer—not when Rolls-Royce is the top of the line and Eisenhower's 1956 Chrysler Imperial is not far down the list. No other dealer can claim to have sold a 24 kt. gold 1920 Pierce Arrow for $180,000; or to having had a customized 1967 Silver Shadow Rolls-Royce pickup truck on display at Neiman-Marcus in Texas.

Mausolf Classic Cars not only sells, but also rents and leases a wide variety of unusual and unique automobiles for movies and TV commercials. So, if your budget is a little tight this month and you can't afford a 1951 Silver Wraith, do the next best thing: rent "Pegasus," a white

Phantom V, and take your friends to dinner—at McDonald's. Ken laughs, but reports that people have done that.

And if, when considering a purchase, you want to kick the tires, we suppose it's okay—but it seems almost sacrilegious.

SEYFER ENGINEERING

7000 Raleigh St.
427-0770

Pride and distinctiveness are not the only benefits to owning a classic car. Compared with the highly touted cars of today, a classic car is usually better built, better driving, and a better investment at the same price.

Helping you derive the most out of your classic car—or helping you find one—is Seyfer Engineering, an award-winning, nationally known automotive specialty shop. Whether you own a classic Rolls Royce, Bentley, Mercedes, Cadillac, Packard, M.G., Pantera, other classic or contemporary vehicles, Seyfer has the background, the highly-experienced craftsmen, and the commitment to properly service or restore your car.

One of the most complete restoration and automotive facilities in the nation, Seyfer has body and paint, chroming, engine rebuilding, chassis fabrication, and tune-up departments, and specialized equipment to handle anything your classic or contemporary car needs.

The chrome shop, experienced in all types of decorative chrome work, specializes in repair and restoration of delicate antique trim pieces. Mechanics in the engine and chassis fabrication departments are imaginative and unparalleled in their ability for exacting detail. The bodyshop personnel are highly experienced craftsmen. Detail and perfection are a must.

Complementing Seyfer's skills are the services of Auto Weave Upholstery, where owner Ron Nelson has the distinctive ability to reproduce the original classic look with the latest in high quality upholstery material.

Seyfer's experience and imaginative work have earned numerous awards for constructing such special interest vehicles as street rods, off-road vehicles, and replica car kits.

Seyfer honors the age-old tradition of craftsmen and connoisseurs—they will not release a vehicle until they are satisfied it meets their highest standards. Whether you own a classic car, are looking for one, or just want general service by skilled professionals, Seyfer Engineering will be happy to talk to you. They have as much pride in their work as you do in your car.

Audio Interiors ltd.

550 S. Colorado Blvd.
321-2837

Also in Oklahoma City
2721 Northwest Expressway
405/843-8339

The name "Audio Interiors" has become well known to owners of fine cars as the place for automotive hi-fi and motoring accessories.

The Audio Interiors approach to the automobile's listening environment is one of engineering . . . then craftsmanship.

High fidelity systems are carefully designed to fit a customer's budget, listening preferences, and the acoustic properties of the car.

Select components from high-end manufacturers, such as Sony, Kenwood, Concord, Audiomobile, and Blaupunkt power hidden networks of home quality speakers by JVC, OHM, Infinity, and Cerwin Vega, among others. Other electronics can be integrated into the car's wiring system, including hidden radar detectors, communications equipment, automatic alarms, sub-woofers, and more.

In addition, complementary quality motoring accessories such as Recaro seats, Momo and Nardi steering wheels, and lambs wool seat covers make your car as comfortable and safe as its sound is pleasing.

With a preferred client club and extended warranties available, Audio Interiors is proof that you can make a sound investment in your car.

AUDIO SMITH AND MOBILE ALARM SYSTEMS

**7925 E. Harvard Ave. #C
696-0930**

When it comes to sound and safety for your automobile, nobody does it better than Audio Smith and Mobile Alarm Systems.

Audio Smith brings more than 40 years' combined experience in automotive electronics and installation. Whether a custom installed sound or security system, they stand by their superior workmanship with a lifetime installation warranty.

Audio Smith can tailor a high quality stereo system to meet your wants and needs. Among the lines they handle is the famous Blaupunkt, the finest auto stereo available.

Audio Smith can install custom speakers, including hand-wound crossover networks to give the listener the finest separation of tweeter, midrange, woofer, and sub-woofer sounds.

To protect that stereo—and your car—Mobile Alarms can install a state-of-the-art security system that will deter even the most determined thief. You can select from a choice of fine basic units or they can custom design one.

Employing the latest in digital computerization, these security systems may include ultrasonic, microwave, motion detection, audio discriminator, or shock-sensing devices. In addition to sounding a loud alarm, the systems can be tied to a convenient paging unit to warn you wherever you are that someone is tampering with your vehicle.

An elaborate luxury, you say? Consider this: an automobile is stolen every 22 seconds in the United States, and in Denver theft and burglary of all kinds is the number one crime.

So why take a chance? Drive to Audio Smith and Mobile Alarm Systems. Let them install great sounds and peace of mind.

Broadcasting

In the mood for your favorite music? Want to know what's happening locally, nationally, internationally—now? Have something you want to speak out on? Looking for entertainment? Tune in to these stations—Denver's finest.

The City and County Building, home to the administrative and judicial branches of the city and county of Denver, lies at the west end of the city's lovely Civic Center. If one stands at its main entrance, the building's two curved wings seem to reach out toward the State Capitol Building three blocks away, as if a gentle reminder of the pressing need for cooperation between city and state. In between lies the formal, park-like Civic Center, its gardens, monuments, fountains, colonnade, and outdoor Greek theater—a popular place for brown baggers and tourists. ⤸ During the Christmas season the City and County Building is a very special place for Denverites, displaying one of the most elaborate lighting decorations in the nation. Christmas also is the time to hear the building's charming carillon bells, which were discovered only recently after being unused for years. ⤸ Begun in 1929 and completed in 1932, the building's low profile preserves the dramatic view of the mountains from the State Capitol. The $4½ million granite office building boasts the largest bronze doors ever cast in the United States. ⤸ Marking the completion of the building was the installation of the Speer Memorial clock and chimes, named for the man most responsible for the office building and the Civic Center, Mayor Robert Speer. ⤸ Ironically, Speer never lived to see his dream fulfilled. He died in 1918 well before excavation for the building began. But the City and County Building, like many other projects visible today, remains an enduring legacy to the man who more than any single person changed the face of Denver.

KOA-TV, Channel 4, Denver's NBC affiliate, is bringing Denver a new commitment, a professionalism dedicated to the highest standards of broadcasting excellence.

KOA-TV is dedicated to making NewsCenter 4 Colorado's news channel. Live, local programming is second to no station in the country. They do this with Colorado's largest broadcast news team, and by offering innovative entertainment programming that is capturing national attention.

At NewsCenter 4 they believe that fast, accurate, pertinent information is the lifeline of Colorado's people. You can see this commitment in the work of such talented NewsCenter 4 professionals as co-anchors George Caldwell and Janet Zappala, and one of Colorado's most honored and experienced newscasters, Bob Palmer.

You can see it in live reports from NewsCenter 4's Western, Northern, Southern, and Boulder Valley Bureaus in Colorado; from their Washington, D.C. Bureau; and live from "Copter 4." You can see it in the NewsCenter 4 Specialists, who offer superior investigative, consumer, entertainment, medical, environmental, and political reporting.

NewsCenter 4 is on the air at 6 a.m., noon, 5 and 10 p.m. There are updates and reports throughout the night on Channel 4's innovative entertainment show, "All Night Live." Rounding out their comprehensive coverage are bright sports reports, exclusive coverage of Denver Bronco games, and accurate, entertaining weather information.

Behind the scenes, NewsCenter 4's new direction and enthusiasm may be less visible but no less important. Spearheading this drive is the station's vice president and general manager, Roger Ogden. With 23 years of broadcast experience in the city, his reputation in TV news has gained national attention.

To assist the news team in covering breaking news, they've acquired the latest in equipment, including a steerable satellite dish for their precedent-setting live coverage from Colorado's Western Slope.

KOA's dedication to Denver and Colorado comes from "native" pride. They've grown up with Denver, as part of an experienced broadcasting family established by the General Electric Company in 1924.

KOA believes in community involvement. They've participated in the March of Dimes telethon, the Vet-a-Thon, and the Special Olympics, to name a few.

NewsCenter 4 is excited about Denver and its future. That's why they are bringing a new commitment today to the city of tomorrow.

KWGN-TV-2 is Denver's *own* television station—committed to the people who want the best in news, sports, and entertainment.

In touch with a changing, growing city, TV-2 recently moved into brand new facilities bristling with the most modern equipment, including a large satellite dish bringing national and international news to Denver homes. With one eye on the world, TV-2 conveniently informs viewers of up-to-the-minute local news, sports, and weather by providing the only prime time newscast in town.

Sports coverage is another reason TV-2 is Denver's own station. When the Nuggets, the Rockies, or the Avalanche start the clock, home and away, Denver viewers are there, *live*. When baseball fills our world, KWGN carries the most exciting major league games, *live*, via satellite, from diamonds across the country.

If you haven't discovered it already, Denver is a sports town. So it's only fitting TV-2 complements its excellent game coverage with a live sports talk program, "Sports Connection," Sunday at 10 p.m. A team of sports-smart regulars and special guests discuss recent games, exchange opinions and predictions, and answer questions from the studio audience and home viewers.

For entertainment, Denverites tune in to TV-2 for their favorite programs throughout the day. Comedy is from 5 to 7, and every evening KWGN presents the best from Hollywood, bringing to you, in prime time, top stars in their winning performances.

Tune into Denver. Tune into KWGN-TV-2. Denver's *own*.

KWGN-TV
DENVER
2

BELIEVES

KMGH-TV DENVER

KMGH-TV's modern and individualized logo, "7 Believes," symbolizes the station's fairness in news coverage, journalistic integrity, community involvement and quality programming. It expresses a conviction and a commitment to the issues deemed most important by the community. The station sponsors the Crimestoppers program to help curtail crime, as well as programs designed to help solve unemployment problems, support the needy, and contribute to a better quality of life for Colorado residents.

Channel 7 is part of McGraw-Hill, an international communications company specializing in information for consumers. Also, as a member of the CBS Television Network, KMGH is able to provide its viewers the kind of quality programming and news CBS has long been noted for.

The station's new state-of-the-art digital video equipment enhances the diversity of on-air video presentations. Local public interests are served through regularly scheduled documentaries and other public affairs programs. Channel 7 has gained recognition for outstanding local programs produced to serve the informational and cultural needs of the community.

News 7 is now setting the pace for local television newscasts. The contemporary set reflects the Denver skyline and provides a true working environment for its professional newscasters. The style of "Live on 7" and "Nightscene" epitomizes television newscasts for the 80s, providing instantaneous coverage and a staff of journalists who not only report the news, but analyze its meaning and future implications.

KMGH-TV also boasts one of the finest production centers in the region, featuring 24-hour-a-day studio and post-production facilities. The production atmosphere promotes the belief that professionalism will result in quality. That quality is evident in both program and commercial production.

The "Research 7 Market Audit" is an exclusive marketing service available at no charge to local businesses. This service provides companies with original and customized research information to help them better position themselves and set realistic marketing goals.

KMGH-TV is involved and dedicated. "7 Believes" is not a slogan, but a standard of dedication, expectation and purpose for Colorado, its residents and its future.

united cable television corporation

A COMPANY WITH EXCEPTIONAL VISIONS.

4700 South Syracuse Parkway
779-5999
Denver, Colorado 80237

Back in 1952, Gene and Richard Schneider, the founders of United Cable Television Corporation, had a vision that both a need and craving for cable TV existed in Casper, Wyoming. Most people there had only heard of television and the nearest station broadcasting over the air was in Denver, more than 250 miles away. Well, the brothers Schneider took action and, as their success indicates, their vision has been perfect.

From these humble beginnings, United Cable has grown to become America's largest independent multiple-system operator dedicated solely to communications. This specialization, rare in the industry, is a major reason for United's widespread reputation for the finest construction, performance, and quality of service available today.

UCTC's continuing leadership is evidenced by its many accomplishments:
- The nation's first cable use of microwave.
- The country's first local cable news service, in 1958.
- The first test of interactive home security over cable, in 1972.
- The successful use of fiber optics, in 1980.
- The first national cable commitment to carry HBO and ESPN
- Twenty-one "ACE" awards and nominations (the cable industry's "Emmy").

In fiscal year 1982, United expects revenues of more than $90 million with an internal cash flow of $35 million. They're big and experienced enough to build any size system anywhere, yet they haven't outgrown their primary objective . . . to be responsive to the communities they serve.

As UCTC looks toward the future, they continue to pioneer new frontiers in the field of cable television. United's INDAX service, the only true two-way, interactive cable television service presently in operation in the United States, includes such futuristic services as banking and shopping in the home.

United Cable Television Corporation owns and operates 37 cable television systems in 84 communities located in 16 states and provides service to more than 455,000 basic subscribers who subscribe to some 368,000 premium services. United recently announced an agreement to acquire up to an 80% interest in Home Entertainment Network, Inc., which currently operates over-the-air subscription TV systems (STV) in the Cincinnati, Dayton and Chicago television markets and will start up another STV operation in Minneapolis-St. Paul during 1982.

United is a publicly held company with over 20,000 stockholders and is the only independent cable television company listed on the New York Stock Exchange.

KVOD

Denver is a rich radio town.
  Rich in history
  Rich in stations.
  Rich in flavor and variety.

But Denver's only full-time classical music station is KVOD. Programmed by a talented, sensitive staff, our voice is conversational and low-key, not highbrow. Our commitments are to excellence, entertainment and integrity. Our promise: never to preach or to take ourselves too seriously.

Within the commitment are several mandates. "Integrity" is not a loose word at KVOD. We never interrupt a complete performance. If something on our air must suffer, let it be the schedule. We'll find enough hours in the day to get everything in, and our masters—L.v Beethoven, W.A. Mozart, and C. Ives among them—will sound all the happier for it.

Denver's radio community has long wondered about the secret of our success. It's gratifying to mingle with

people and consistently hear the comment, "I only listen to two radio stations, KVOD and . . ." The most gratifying thing, of course, is that the *other* station is seldom twice the same, that it might be at the top or bottom of either radio dial, from all-news to jazz. This proves what we've long known: the KVOD audience has diverse tastes and interests. Our survey tells us it's an educated audience. KVOD listeners generally make good money, but aren't exclusive to any income bracket. By

and large, they own their homes, read books, go to restaurants, attend films, recitals and art exhibits. They cross the whole spectrum of maturity, with our largest audience ranging between 25 and 65 years old.

Our air staff is another reason for our success. Gene Amole has been a fixture in Denver radio for more years than he likes to remember. John Wolfe, in addition to his studio duties, has developed the interview to a fine art form, making "In The Square" an informative

noonday break. Terry McDonald, Jake Williams, John and Charley Samson, Dick Brehm and Maggie Welch combine knowledge and warmth to fill out the KVOD schedule.

The schedule includes opera from the Met, Chicago Lyric Opera and Houston Grand Opera. There are regular symphonic broadcasts by the Boston Pops, New York Philharmonic, Chicago, Cleveland, San Francisco and Denver Symphony Orchestras. Each weekday Karl Haas, musicologist extraordinaire, offers music and commentary. "Preview" and "First Hearing" review new classical records. There is music from the BBC and from Radio Nederland. And on "America in Concert," the KVOD audience experiences lesser known orchestras.

Audience. Staff. Diversity. Warmth. And of course the masters.

There's no one secret of our success. But there is just one KVOD.

And Denver is richer for it.

WILLIAM K. SWARTZ

All news all the time has proven to be a successful formula at KDEN Newsradio 1340. Reaching a 100% adult audience, KDEN Newsradio concentrates on delivering a continuing stream of news and information to motivated, concerned people who want to stay abreast of daily activities in an ever changing world.

"We find that the people who want to stay ahead want to be fully informed in order to be able to meet the challenges of today's world," says KDEN Newsradio president, Doug Stephens. "Research shows that these people tend to be upwardly mobile adults over 25, above average in education, and earning well above average incomes."

KDEN Newsradio broadcasts what amounts to 48 newspapers a day, each updated from the one preceding it. During certain time periods, such Lifestyle segments as *Chef Pierre, The Grapevine, Green and Growing, Trendsetters,* and *Showbiz with Jo Farrell,* are featured. From early morning to evening, hourly satellite reports from The Wall Street Journal are aired.

For an advertiser, KDEN Newsradio presents some special opportunities. Unlike any music format, KDEN Newsradio requires a high attention level, benefitting advertisers whose messages are on the station.

"KDEN Newsradio has a substantial history of success," says Stephens. "We think Denver has a tremendous future and we're excited to be part of it. And we look forward to telling the story of that future as it unfolds."

KDEN
News 1340

KEZW am 1430

Glenn Miller. . .Patti Page. . .Neil Diamond. . .Perry Como. . .Lynn Anderson. . .Benny Goodman. . .Peggy Lee . . .Elvis Presley. . .Harry James. . .

What do these singers and musicians all have in common? They represent the music of your life.

That's what KEZW AM 1430 is all about. The top hits of the 40s, 50s, 60s, and 70s. The music of your life. The music that's as fresh as the day it was first played. The music that never dies.

Promotional fluff? No, that's KEZW listeners talking. Their response to KEZW has proved to the station and its advertisers that the easy-time music still lives.

When KEZW sponsored the first of its series of big band concerts, more than 1,000 tickets to the "one and only" Tommy Dorsey Orchestra sold out in a few days. Such bands as Glenn Miller and Les Brown continue to draw similar excitement.

KEZW's popular on-the-air personalities receive the same enthusiastic response. From Bob Meyer's "get up and go show" to Diane Dixon's love affair with her "night people," the requests roll in.

Play "Mister Sandman."

"As Time Goes By."

"Sentimental Journey."

"Mona Lisa."

Play the music of your life.

KLIR FM 100

KLIR FM 100 is music for all your moods.

Do you need to unwind? Want to sing? Feel like dancing? Working? Playing?

Whatever your mood, turn on Denver's soft sound. KLIR is one of the metropolitan area's most listened-to music stations, the station that establishes the musical environment of a great city.

Since 1962, KLIR has meant the best in carefully selected and carefully programmed music. Its 100,000-watt coverage of the metropolitan area and enthusiastic listener response has resulted in KLIR being included on a regional cable serving thousands of subscribers in Colorado, Nebraska, and Wyoming.

People of all ages, all incomes, all facets of life love good music.

KLIR delivers.

24 hours a day.

Denver's soft sound.

KLIR FM 100.

KOA NEWS TALK 85

KOA Radio 85 is Denver's premier radio station.

For nearly six decades, KOA has been Denver's Full-Service Radio. Denver's 24 hour news/talk station. For people who want to know what's happening, to whom, why, and how it concerns them.

KOA provides extensive and informative news coverage, programming large blocks of news morning, noon, and evening. Sports, farm and ranch news, hourly updates of local, regional, national, and international news continue around the clock.

Got something on your mind? Speak out on KOA's two-way talk shows. Provocative talk hosts dish up a delectable variety of stimulating topics and viewpoints, ranging from everyday practical matters to subjects shaking the world.

Prominent guests often join in, speaking out in their areas of expertise. Whatever the subject, day or all night, KOA talk shows are sure to be candid, thought-provoking, informative, inspiring, and entertaining.

On the weekends, KOA offers special talk shows for teens, and on such diverse subjects as gardening, automobile maintenance, real estate, cooking, home repairs, and religion.

Sports is covered nowhere better than at KOA. Play-by-play broadcasts of Denver Broncos, Nuggets, Bears, and other championship sports are KOA exclusives. And what avid sports fan can turn down the chance to talk about his favorite sport on the daily Sportstalk?

KOA Radio 85. The radio station for people who care about what's happening.

Q103FM RADIO

KOAQ . . . Q103 FM is the contemporary hit radio station that listens to you.

Q103 doesn't throw music on the air and hope you'll like it. They talk to you first, taking local surveys to learn exactly what *you* want to hear—and that's what they play.

Today's top hits are mixed liberally with your favorite oldies ("music you grew up with") to be sure that the music reflects your tastes and pleasures.

It is played by top radio personalities, 24 hours a day, transmitted from high on Lookout Mountain,

bringing Q103 listeners the clearest, strongest signal possible.

That's the main event. Here are the fringe benefits of this fine mainstream FM station.

Q103 keeps its fans up to date with the latest concert information. Dinners at luxurious restaurants, beautiful jewelry, vacation trips for the family, weekends at exotic locations, concert and movie tickets and dozens of other prizes are awarded the year 'round to Q103 fans—just for listening.

Audience participation is a must for

one of Denver's favorite radio features, Q103's "Dateline," heard every Friday morning. You can call in, describe yourself, and describe the person you're looking for in your life. You may join the scores of Q103 listeners who have had interesting successful dates. Even a marriage or two have come from "Dateline."

Q103 is part of the KOA family, along with KOA Radio 85 and KOA-TV. It's a family dedicated to complete radio and television service. A family that listens to you.

Finance & Investments

Financial security is more important than ever in these times of high inflation, high interest rates, and high unemployment. You can feel secure in patronizing any of these sound financial institutions.

Seventeenth Street. ✒ *A stroll through this canyon of steel and glass and power reveals why the street is often referred to as "The Wall Street of the Rockies." Banks, investment firms, insurance companies, real estate brokers, and corporate headquarters jockey for position on this most prestigious address in Denver, sometimes paying several hundred dollars a square foot for the privilege.* ✒ *A writer could use the street as the title of a novel, so influential has been its wealth and power in the shaping of 20th century Denver. Prior to World War I and well into the 1940s, Seventeenth Street held a reputation as a fiscally conservative men's club. The city reflected that outlook: prosperous yet quick, complacent, provincial.* ✒ *World War II changed all that. Ex-servicemen who had seen this bucolic town flocked to Denver along with job seekers in the late '40s, and nothing could stem the tide of their aspirations. The old Seventeenth Street patriarchs crumbled. New financiers stepped forward to lure such clean, technical industries as electronics, aerospace equipment, and photography. They developed Colorado's oil industry and recruited regional federal agencies.* ✒ *With the onset of the 1980s, Denver is emerging as the energy capitol of the West and Seventeenth Street is its financial and commercial brain. Hundreds of firms have made Denver their base of operations as they search the rich Rocky Mountain empire for oil and shale, natural gas, uranium, and coal. Developers, caught up in the boom, have poured $2 billion in just three years into changing the face of downtown Denver.* ✒ *Excitement not seen since the early gold rush days has captured this city. And nowhere has the change been more dramatic than on Seventeenth Street.*

CENTURY BANK

First of Denver

621 17th Street
893-2211

The First National Bank of Denver Plaza has become widely known as the downtown "people place." It has become a gathering spot for shoppers and workers alike as they marvel at Denver's dramatic growth and watch the profusion of activities that take place each year on the plaza.

The plaza's popularity is no surprise to those familiar with Denver. First of Denver has been people-oriented since it was chartered in 1865 as Denver's first bank.

Today, First of Denver is one of the Rocky Mountain region's largest financial institutions. It is the lead bank of the $3 billion First National Bancorporation and provides a full range of banking services—corporate, trust and retail.

First of Denver has been instrumental in Denver's continued economic growth and continues to maintain a special understanding of the commercial and industrial growth needs, particularly in the areas of Denver's most spectacular growth, real estate construction and energy. The bank is the largest commercial-industrial lender in the Rocky Mountain region, and the 80th largest in the nation.

The bank's trust department also is the largest in the region, managing more than $1.4 billion in assets and featuring one of the nation's top investment teams. Its management of Fund E, an employee pension and profit sharing fund, was among the top 10 performing commingled funds in the nation in 1980 and 1981.

While First of Denver is a leader in commercial-industrial lending, the bank also offers a complete range of consumer services. Standard checking and savings accounts, "NOW" accounts, All-Savers Certificates, IRA/Keogh Accounts, credit cards and high yielding time and money market certificates are available.

In addition, First of Denver developed TransAction Banking, a statewide network of nearly 50 automated, 24-hour teller machines. More than 52 financial institutions across Colorado share the network.

First of Denver: it's a people place.

17th & Champa
893-1862

Colorado National Bank, one of Denver's largest and most innovative banks, has a reputation for making "big ideas happen."

But a reputation like that doesn't develop overnight. Colorado National, in fact, is one of the state's oldest banks, founded in 1862.

It didn't even look like a bank when Luther Kountze rented a corner of Cheesman's Drug Store on 15th Street and began to help make big ideas happen for the boom town's gold prospectors and merchants.

Eventually Kountze's bank built its own home and in 1866 received its national charter under the name Colorado National Bank.

Born of gold and nourished by railroads, Denver emerged as a commercial center of the Rocky Mountain region. Colorado National grew with it, emerging as a major financial force.

By 1915, after moving twice again, Colorado National moved into a home big enough for the future, downtown at 17th and Champa Streets. Though altered and enlarged since then, the basic structure still stands, with its classic Greek pillars, terrazzo marble interior, and the fourteen Allen True murals on the walls of the lobby symbolizing the American Indian's self-portrayed cycle of life.

The bank's physical structure has changed little since then, but its financial strength and commitment to Denver has never ceased growing. Colorado National has helped nurture the region through the Great Depression and two world wars.

Today it leads the way as the region booms into the energy-conscious '80s. A modern, innovative, professional team of bankers at Colorado National Bank is playing a major role in the financial success of Colorado, its citizens and businesses.

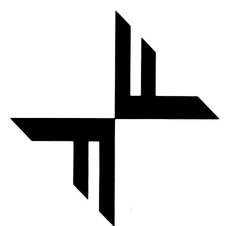

First Federal Savings

215 S. Wadsworth
232-2121

Monday-Friday 9-5; Saturday 9-1

A history of First Federal Savings is necessarily a reflection of the Collier family. Pioneer photographer Joseph Collier was one of the founders of the Cooperative Savings and Loan Association, which officially opened on April 25, 1885. Seven other building and loan associations were listed in the 1885 Denver City Directory, but First Federal is the only survivor of the eight operating at that time.

Joseph Collier was nominated to the board of directors, but declined to serve. But his son, Robert, served First Federal in various capacities, ranging from attorney to director, for many years.

With the granting of a federal charter on March 6, 1934, the Cooperative Association was renamed First Federal Savings. That same year a Certificate of Insurance was granted by the Federal Savings and Loan Insurance Corporation.

Robert's son, Malcolm E. Collier, served as its President from 1939 to 1972.

A more progressive growth resulted after the election of Malcolm Collier, Jr., as president in 1972. Since that time First Federal Savings has expanded to 15 offices in metro Denver and Brighton, Louisville, Greeley and Fort Lupton, with assets totaling over $450 million.

Despite being the eighth largest savings and loan association in Colorado, First Federal has always maintained a policy of safety and stability instead of size. Controlled growth, a strong net worth, profitability, and conservative management are still the primary objectives.

First Federal offers a full range of services—passbook savings accounts, mortgage and consumer loans, certificates of deposit, interest-bearing checking with overdraft protection, everything a savings and loan can offer under the rules governing it by federal mandate.

First Federal Savings may be the oldest in Colorado, but it's still one of the most vigorous.

COLORADO FEDERAL

A SAVINGS AND LOAN ASSOCIATION

MEMBER
FSLIC
Federal Savings & Loan Insurance Corp.

Your Savings Insured to $100,000

821 17th Street
524-4241

When the new Ideal Cement Building was completed in 1907, it was recognized as one of Colorado's most impressive structures. It was the first reinforced concrete building west of the Mississippi, and the finest local artists and craftsmen designed and produced its distinguished decor.

In 1927, the building's name was changed to Denver National Bank Building. Most of the interior art work was begun in that year.

With another change in ownership, in 1959, the name reverted to a shorter version of the original — the Ideal Building.

In 1976, Colorado Federal Savings found it had outgrown its existing facilities. In looking for a new location, it was desirable that the building portray an image of stability and quality. The building now named Colorado Federal Building fit all the requirements.

With the purchase of the building, Colorado Federal made a commitment to refurbish, restore and preserve a Denver landmark. First, the original marble and stucco exterior was restored. Then, the main lobby's one-ton, cast bronze doors and elaborate relief ceiling were returned to their former elegance. Marble and terrazzo floors were uncovered and refinished. The unique art work and elaborate ceilings were repaired and repainted. Marble columns were polished and a sculpted frieze depicting the history of money was cleaned and restored. New fixtures were crafted and installed to match the existing wood decor. In short — a grand old building was reborn.

Colorado Federal is proud that its efforts led to placing the Colorado Federal Building in the National Register of Historic Places, and invites everyone to come in and view part of Historical Denver.

Colorado Federal Savings and Loan Association is as solid and stable as the building that houses its main office. Established in 1920, it offers a full range of financial services there or at any of its six branch offices.

Colorado Federal — preserving and making history on 17th Street.

WILLIAM K. SWARTZ

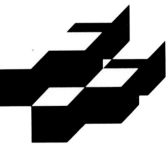

First Financial Securities, Inc.

One Park Central
1515 Arapahoe Street, Suite 1585
534-7777 or
Call toll free 1-800-525-6107

Denver has been called the "Boom Town of the '80s" by many people, and First Financial Securities, Inc. can help you understand and take advantage of the many growing opportunities in our region. Any investment firm depends on its people for success, and at First Financial, people are the most valuable energy asset.

From "lights on" at 7:00 a.m. to "lights off" at 9:00 p.m., the people at First Financial are working to research, collect and sift through information about the many over-the-counter stock issues available today. These issues include high technology computers, medical devices, communication companies and energy stocks. Since the speculative element is more prominent in OTC trading, customers should have the opportunity to make sound judgments based on facts.

First Financial employs a highly trained research staff to look into upcoming trends and possible opportunities. Plus, at First Financial there is a full-time CPA and legal counselor. Their talents and expertise offer another facet to the research available for clients.

As a member of the New York Stock Exchange, First Financial can offer its clients a wide range of investment opportunities.

Commercial Design

Getting the most for the building dollar is a critical task for many companies. Innovative, energy-smart design and sound, economical construction are fundamental. So we've culled the very best architects, consulting engineers, and construction firms to help you build a better Denver.

When the 21-story Daniels and Fisher Tower was completed in 1911, she was the third tallest structure in the United States and the tallest west of the Missisippi. Today, she stands like a waif, her brick facade and quaint hand-wound tower clock overshadowed by the tall, shiny "plazas" and "centers" and "towers" sprouting up in a city that could easily adopt the building crane as its official seal. ❧ Yes, the changes in the Denver skyline in recent years have been extraordinary. Yet the D&F Tower remains standing with a dignity and grace that has always made her a favorite of residents and visitors alike. ❧ The tower was built as the main entrance to a new Daniels and Fisher department store, which had long catered to Denver's elite. The tower's unusual architecture was inspired by the Campanile of St. Mark's in Venice. Visitors flocked to her observation balcony, which afforded a 200-mile view of the Rocky Mountain range. Fittingly, the doorman to the tower for nearly half a century was a 7 foot 3 inch giant named Carl Sandell, as much a landmark as the tower herself. ❧ Until the 1950s, the D&F Tower remained the tallest structure in Denver, the sole exception to a 12-story height ordinance imposed 40 years before to preserve the city's view of the Front Range. When the ordinance gave way in the fifties the tower quickly paled, and by 1965 her doom appeared imminent. The remainder of the Daniels and Fisher department store was razed in 1971, but fortunately the tower survived as Denver citizens rallied to her side. ❧ Eventually the tower was declared a historic landmark. Luxury offices now occupy her interior but the familiar exterior remains unchanged, a reminder to all those tall new city slickers just who Denver's first skyscraper really was.

Richard Weingardt Consultants

Structural and Civil Engineers
625 E. 16th
Denver, CO 80203

Richard Weingardt Consultants Inc. is a full-service structural/civil engineering firm that has achieved a dual reputation for its expert, award-winning work and for its public-spirited contributions to Denver.

Founded in 1965 by Richard Weingardt, RWC provides technical services for architects, contractors, private industry and governmental agencies. In addition to structural design services, RWC provides civil and industrial engineering and surveying.

Using its thorough knowledge of the latest engineering technology, the firm has prepared feasibility, systems analysis and cost comparison studies, and investigations for engineering design and construction.

RWC has an impressive record for meeting deadlines and budgets with fresh, innovative approaches. The firm has completed engineering projects in more than 35 states and several foreign countries, ranging from high-rise buildings to municipal facilities, bridges and subdivisions. In engineering three 200-foot feedmill towers in the U.S.S.R., for instance, RWC designed a floating mat foundation because of poor soil conditions and locally high seismic activity.

Several RWC projects have received engineering awards, including Colorado Consulting Engineers Council awards for Denver projects such as the International Athletic Club, American National Bank Parking Garage, Mount Olivet Administration Building and skylights for the Denver Center for the Performing Arts. In 1981, they received one of two masonry Awards of Excellence for masonry structures constructed in Colorado in the last decade.

With a commitment to community as well as engineering excellence, RWC has in the past decade worked on more than two dozen restoration and renovation projects involving historic buildings in Denver. Richard Weingardt has also sponsored community interest seminars such as a recent wind seminar, focusing on how to design and build high-rise structures so that Denver won't become another windy city, perilous to pedestrians.

At RWC, engineering is concerned ultimately with people.

the hoffmann partnership inc

1439 Larimer St.
572-0507

Creating an environment requires skills found in only a few design firms. The professionals at The Hoffman Partnership, Inc. (HPI) are experienced in architecture, interior design, graphic design, master planning, engineering, project development, and site selection and acquisition.

In the past 15 years, HPI has grown from a small group of architects to a full service design firm with offices in Denver, St. Louis and Columbus, Ohio. They're proud of the fact that 60 percent of their clients are repeat customers.

HPI projects have ranged from a $3,500 office interior to an $80 million medical complex. Project design experience includes banks, schools, university buildings, historic restorations, hotels, shopping centers, hospitals, offices, parking structures, warehouses, industrial manufacturing facilities, and research laboratories.

One of the more distinctive projects is the national headquarters of the Arabian Horse Trust and Registry in Denver, Colorado. A considerable challenge confronted the HPI design team, since the project would house the headquarters for three distinctive organizations. The finished work includes flexible office areas, museum and archives, research library, audio-visual viewing room, and computer facilities.

The Hoffmann Partnership excels in translating clients' goals into reality. The individual talents of the people of HPI are complemented by their interest in new ideas. They believe these abilities allow them to develop a sense of teamwork between the client and themselves— a necessity for a successful project.

Left to right: Jim Smith, Tim Reed, Gary Ross, Jim Kirts and David Sanders.

RNL Architects and Planners

Rogers Nagel Langhart
1576 Sherman Street
Denver, CO 80203
832-5599

Each client has building and site conditions requiring a special solution. RNL believes mutual communication and commitment is the essence of their quality design process.

As technologies, environmental concerns and energy considerations become more complex and sophisticated, it is important to RNL as professionals to bring all the decision makers together at the beginning of the design process. Their urban planning projects are successful using these techniques in conjunction with community relationships.

This process is effective for exploring and evaluating alternative concepts as part of the decision-making process, providing early and continuous cost control.

They believe it is important to relate a structure to its site and neighboring buildings, as well as the consideration of internal functions, economic considerations and other client objectives.

Owens-Corning Fiberglas Corporation recognized RNL's energy-conscious designs by bestowing on the firm one of its Energy Conservation awards for the design of the Denver RTD bus maintenance facility. The bus garage is one of the largest air solar-heated buildings in the country.

RNL is a full-service architectural and planning firm, one of the oldest and largest in the Rocky Mountain region, affirming a commitment to the healthy and progressive growth of the whole region, as well as Denver.

Top photo: Mountain Bell Tower, Vail. Bottom photo: Wickliff & Company's 1700 Grant Office Building, Denver.

Al Cohen Construction Company

**2505 18th Street
Denver, CO 80211
455-8800**

When businesses need a new home, and need it quickly, they come to Al Cohen Construction. Davis Oil, Samsonite, American Express, Pentax, the Royal Bank of Canada, Rocky Mountain Energy Company, and The Wall Street Journal are among the more than 550 businesses since 1952 who have chosen to build with Al Cohen Construction.

Al Cohen is celebrating its 30th year as a nationally-recognized, full-service general contractor, listed among the top 100 contractors in the nation. It has handled all types of commercial construction, excels in corporate facilities construction and oversees construction management and interior finish functions.

Based in Denver, Al Cohen Construction has shared in the city's dramatic growth, including building 15 highrises. With the completion of its new offices, and expanded capabilities and client services, the company anticipates its growth will match the city's and the West's.

Instrumental to the company's success is its negotiated, team approach to construction. This team approach guides the client from early design phases through final occupancy with "hands on" management techniques, thus minimizing costs and assuring the best building for the construction dollar. Its vast experience enables a client to formulate a sound budget early on, eliminating unpleasant surprises. The construction team works on a fast track schedule, all the while maintaining a high standard of building excellence.

Al Cohen Construction's unequaled record speaks for itself. States one satisfied client: "They're large enough to do the job, small enough to do it well."

The Amoco Building, downtown Denver

JAY SIMON

The First of Denver Plaza Building

Hensel Phelps Construction Co.

General Office:
420 6th Avenue
Greeley, CO 80632
352-6565

Denver Office:
817 17th Street, Suite 704
Denver, CO 80202
595-8100

Hensel Phelps is a diversified general contracting firm growing with Denver, the Rocky Mountain region and the nation.

Working from negotiated and competitive bidding, Hensel Phelps has built highrise office and condominium buildings, hotels, mountain resorts, hospitals, airports, industrial manufacturing facilities, dams, bridges and wastewater treatment plants.

Called "one of the most successful firms in Colorado" by *Colorado Business* magazine, Hensel Phelps has built a 45-year reputation for meeting or exceeding schedules within budget at specified quality standards.

Every industry has its pacesetters, a small group recognized for consistently superior performance. In the highly competitive construction industry, where such recognition is particularly difficult to earn, Hensel Phelps Construction Co. has established a solid reputation for leadership.

They welcome the opportunity to participate in your project as general contractor.

Stellar Plaza, Denver

SLP
A Professional Corporation

623-7031

The philosophy of SLP is one of innovation tempered by realism and flexibility. A team approach to each project, with staff members working together from conception through completion assures a design solution that reflects the client's needs and contributes positively to the human environment.

The firm's expertise includes planning, interior design, interior space planning and landscape architecture in addition to architectural services for a variety of project types—educational facilities, professional office buildings, shopping centers, residential projects, parking structures, recreational centers, medical facilities, churches and health centers. Currently located in the historic Equitable Building in downtown Denver, they have been involved with the restoration of many of Denver's landmark buildings.

Since the firm's inception, they have maintained their offices in the downtown area. They take pride in being a part of the community and have achieved a reputation as a firm with a lasting commitment to Denver. This is being confirmed by their planned move to Terracentre, a building of their own design, at Stout and Speer.

Top left: Farm Credit Banks Headquarters   Left: The Anaconda Tower, Denver Square
Right: Rocky Mountain Energy Company Headquarters

Flack + Kurtz
Consulting engineers
Denver office:
1425 Market St.
Denver, CO 80202
825-0100

Also serving cities of the region
and beyond:
San Francisco
Dallas/Ft. Worth
Minneapolis/St. Paul
Seattle
Phoenix
Kansas City
New Orleans
San Antonio
Tucson
Oklahoma City
Tulsa
Salt Lake City
Los Angeles

In Denver, the award-winning firm of Flack + Kurtz Consulting Engineers has been involved in numerous projects; among them, the energy-conscious Rocky Mountain Energy Headquarters Building, the Anaconda Tower, the Amoco Building, and the impressive Great West Life Center pictured on the cover of this publication.

As a full-service mechanical and electrical engineering firm, Flack + Kurtz has earned a reputation for innovative design and commitment to professional integrity. The company has performed major consulting and design contracts for government agencies, medical and educational institutions, and private corporations.

It offers complete mechanical, electrical, sanitary, life safety, energy analysis, construction administration, research-development, and building management services.

Flack + Kurtz has been a pioneer in energy conservation, including utilizing alternative energy resources. In recognizing their work, Owens-Corning Fiberglas Corporation placed Flack + Kurtz in the vanguard of applied energy-saving technology when it awarded one of its 1981 Energy Conservation Awards for the design of the Farm Credit Banks Building in Spokane, Washington.

With offices in Denver and around the country, Flack + Kurtz can draw on a vast network of resources to meet the most complex design challenges. The firm is currently designing projects in all of the major cities in the region.

Real Estate

Living in Colorado is an enviable experience, made all the more pleasurable by the selection of the right home. Let these firms help you make the selection that will make Denver and Colorado your home for life.

Below marshmallow clouds, gaudy sailboats skim lazily across the reservoir's glistening waters. Nearby, campers pitch their tents and head for the swimming beach. Fishermen probe intently for walleye, trout and bass. Horseback riders saunter along ten miles of trails, catching vistas of the Front Range. ⤳ Cherry Creek state Recreational Area is the playground for southeast Denver, with 1½ million visitors each year. Located at I-225 and Parker Road, the reservoir's facilities include a marina, six miles of bicycle trail, a 74-unit campground, gun range, picnic grounds, and even a model airplane field. In the winter, the 880-acre lake is popular for ice boating, skating, and ice fishing. ⤳ The U.S. Army Corps of Engineers built Cherry Creek Dam in the early fifties to control the temperamental Cherry Creek, which had burst its banks several times during Denver's history. But too much water is less a problem to the Queen City than too little. The dam is also part of a vast network of dams, tunnels, reservoirs, canals, and pumping stations designed to divert and store water for communities on the Front Range and for irrigation of farms. ⤳ Since Denver was founded, the quest for adequate water supplies has been relentless and not without considerable technological, legal, and political controversy. Much of Denver area water has been siphoned from the more water-rich western slope of the Rockies. As far back as 1860 water was diverted to the Front Range for mining. Since then transmountain water diversions have included the Moffat Tunnel, Colorado-Big Thompson project, and the huge Blue River diversion. Without these water diversions, Denver and the surrounding communities could easily have withered and died on an unforgiving dry plain. ⤳ The demand for still more water remains high, and in the face of projected population growth relief appears unlikely. Cries of no-growth versus more growth, conservation versus more dam building, continue to rage. Whatever one's viewpoint, however, all sides concur on one point: for Denver and the Front Range, water is the lifeblood.

W. MUENSTERMANN

123

11853 Pecos St.
469-7848

There was a time when the West of our imagination was big skies and open spaces and a horizon full of mountains. At The Ranch, it still is.

The Ranch is the first exclusive master-planned community of its kind northwest of Denver. Set in a country club atmosphere, these luxurious, award-winning estate sites and homes are establishing new standards for community living.

Recognizing another outstanding development by the Winn Group, many Denver area home builders have constructed prestigious homes at The Ranch. Some are contemporary, some traditional. All are imaginative, all in harmony with each other and with the land. Like the West of our imagination, The Ranch is big enough to embrace a variety of tastes and lifestyles.

The Ranch is the place to build your dream home. Some Ranch owners have brought in their own architect. Others have chosen from the variety of plans offered by the carefully chosen builders. Yet another option is a completed home. Possibilities include a two-story, award-winning home featuring a luxurious outdoor hot tub, three fireplaces, three bedrooms, and 2½ baths. Or try a 6,400-square-foot Spanish style home with colonnaded courtyard, beamed ceilings and sky-

the Ranch

lights, five bedrooms, a spectacular bar. Anything is feasible at The Ranch.

Many of the builders are taking advantage of Colorado's bountiful sunshine, incorporating energy-saving features such as passive solar. Each home is set on spacious, oversize lots, commanding an inspiring view of the Front Range of the Rockies.

The Ranch has spared nothing in the quality of their homes, but they believe you should be spared the high cost of financing. The homes are offered at below-market interest rates.

The Ranch has been so meticulously planned, so committed to quality and affordable acquisition that it swept the 1980 sales awards by the Home Builders Association of Metropolitan Denver, capturing "best custom home" and "best interior design" designations, and the grand award as "community of the year"!

This dedication to detail and concept at The Ranch is coupled with natural recreational amenities that make the 420-acre community one of the most fashionable places to live along the Front Range.

More than one third of the land has intentionally been left undeveloped to preserve the quiet, park-like atmosphere, the wooded glens, lush meadows, the natural lakes and ponds. A sense of serenity pervades The Ranch. This is country living without country hardships.

If you're looking for activity, there's The Ranch Country Club, converted from a baronial estate of the once-flamboyant Fred Ward. Its 18-hole championship golf course has hosted state tournaments and proved the bane of many an unwary golfer, with water hazards on nine holes and bunkers flanking every green. There are lighted tennis courts, saunas and whirlpools, and a 25-meter swimming pool. The Club also contains an exceptional restaurant, a cozy lounge, ballroom, and several meeting rooms.

The Ranch is convenient to shopping centers and malls, theaters, libraries, schools, and medical facilities. Boulder is 20 minutes away, Stapleton International Airport less than 20, downtown Denver only 15, and of course the first tee is but 15 seconds away from your home!

For additional recreation, nearby Barr Lake features some of the state's finest sailing, fishing, and other activities. And with I-25 only a mile away, the magnificent Rockies are within easy reach.

The Ranch is a place of rich history as well as progress, symbolized by the massive white, red-roofed barn with its towering windmill. The land was originally homesteaded by the sole survivor of the Battle of the Little Big Horn, whose descendants still live in the area.

That same sense of adventure, of limitless horizons and open space, still lives. At The Ranch.

Genesee

24426 Currant Drive
Golden, Colorado 80401
526-0601

It isn't often that one has the opportunity to savor the best of two worlds. But that's the gift of Genesee, a residential community nestled in the foothills of the Rockies near Denver. Close to the cultural, career, and shopping amenities of a large city, Genesee residents live privately amidst a superb natural environment with clean bracing air and unmatched vistas of America's most beautiful mountains.

Each homesite is located in the rolling mountain community amidst groves of pine, fir, and aspen, or in lush meadows rich in wildflowers and grasses. Approximately one half of Genesee's 2,000 acres will forever be preserved as open space to be shared by the residents. Located between 7,150 and 7,735 feet above sea level, Genesee residents enjoy cool summers and mild winters.

Genesee offers much within its own boundaries. The Vista Clubhouse and the Foothills Clubhouse provide swimming pools, party and game rooms, tennis courts, racquetball-handball courts, steam baths, Jacuzzi, and an exercise room. There is also a jogging trail, hiking trails, tot lots, and picnic areas. Adjacent to the residential community is the Genesee Business Center with professional and corporate office buildings, and restaurants.

Genesee Foundation, the homeowners association, is responsible for roving security guard services and maintenance of private roads and recreational facilities. An architectural review committee insures that high architectural standards are maintained throughout the mountain community.

For those occasions when one yearns for activities outside the community, Genesee is conveniently located near Interstate-70. Denver is only twenty minutes away, Evergreen and Golden less. Many of the state's finest ski areas such as Vail, Winter Park, and Copper Mountain are only an hour to an hour and a half away.

Genesee is the best of both worlds. It is what mountain living was meant to be.

RIDGEWOOD

6350 Coal Mine Road
Littleton
979-4900

In every community there are a few recognized leaders, of outstanding reputation, in home development. In the Denver area, one of the names you will hear again and again is Ridgewood Realty, Inc.

Since its inception more than 20 years ago, Ridgewood has been an out-of-the-ordinary developer. Ridgewood is also a planner, setting the style and tone of the community to be built, and maintaining its deep involvement through all stages of development.

Applewood Grove was Ridgewood's first community. It was selected as the site of the 1959 Home Builders Association Parade of Homes, and is still considered one of the finest suburban Denver areas.

That pattern of success was continued with the development of the Applewood Grove Shopping Center; 500 homes in Applewood Knolls; and Green Mountain Estates, which became the site of the 1962 Parade of Homes.

Typical of Ridgewood's long-term commitment is "Columbine Territory." Begun in 1964, and host to the 1976 Parade of Homes, it is an ongoing project in southern Jefferson County. A community of quiet residential neighborhoods nestled against the foothills, Columbine Territory offers a diversity difficult to match anywhere. Seventeen of the area's best builders have developed nearly 50 different plans in four distinct neighborhoods.

The Estates at Sixth Avenue West is Ridgewood's most distinctive community to date. Unique executive homes dot the rolling foothills. And yet, despite the feeling of "out-of-town" living, The Estates is just twenty minutes from downtown and thirty from the airport.

Ridgewood's professional and experienced sales staff in the Littleton Columbine offices and the Golden Estates office offer expert services in both new homes and in resales. And, 1982 will see the opening of Ridgewood's East Hampden Club in Aurora.

You can count on Ridgewood Realty, Inc., no matter what your family needs.

by Writer

Townhomes:

Chambers Ridge in Aurora	695-1132
Cherry Creek Meadows in Denver	750-6990
Quincy Hill in Aurora	693-1340
Willow Creek in Englewood	770-7990
Hearthstone at South Park	797-0608

Single-family homes:

Sunset Ridge at Ken-Caryl	978-1060
Willow Creek in Englewood	770-6630
Meadowglen in Arvada	420-2226
SouthPark in Littleton	798-3668
Cimarron at Ken-Caryl	973-0119

The "something special" that describes each Writer community is achieved through Writer's mastery of what it takes to make single-family or townhome living no less than exceptional.

It begins with knowing what buyers desire in a home: quality construction and solid craftsmanship, using the finest materials; architectural flair for added interest and elegance; and practical innovation, to meet rising buyer expectations.

It's called "adding value." A knowledge of how to blend progressive design, quality construction and superior land planning to produce attractive, functional homes in a variety of price ranges.

Writer communities have Olympic-size swimming pools to splash in . . . tennis courts for a friendly game of doubles with neighbors . . . pleasant greenbelts and walkways ideal for relaxing strolls . . . clubhouses for social gatherings and bridge tournaments. Two Writer communities are at magnificent Ken-Caryl Ranch, which offers soccer, horseback riding, camping, hiking and cross-country skiing in 4,000 acres of natural open space next to the foothills.

Each Writer community is easily accessible to employment centers, fine entertainment, dining and shopping. Their carefully-chosen locations take advantage of unique geographic features—beautiful lakefront settings, a scenic bluff backdropped by the Rockies—or existing recreation areas such as Cherry Creek Reservoir and the Highline Canal.

The sum of many notable Writer features makes a home great: wood-beamed volume ceilings, large baths with oversize tubs, detailed brick fireplaces, bright skylights. Cozy master bedrooms with separate bath and dressing area. Spacious living areas with exciting variations in floor levels.

The Writer Corporation meets the challenge of bringing all these essential elements together to create beautiful communities. In every respect—home features, setting, quality, esthetics, price, recreation—Writer's comprehensively-planned communities are really something special.

WRITER SQUARE

Writer Square: a pleasant change of pace for those desiring sophisticated retail establishments and restaurants that are something special!

Linking historic Larimer Square and Denver's new 16th Street Shopping Mall, Writer Square offers an exciting mix of boutiques, shops and eating establishments, all built around charming European-style plazas accented by brick archways and a romantic clock tower. Stroll amidst trees, colorful flowers and gaslight lamps while shopping. Writer Square is urbanity with an unexpected touch of nature!

At Writer Square, you're assured of finding the new-and-unusual you seek... as well as the tried-and-true. Order up a refreshing drink and a steaming bowl of chili with all the delicious extras you can imagine! Or relax on a plaza bench with a tantalizing double-decker ice-cream cone!

Select a sweater or tie for any occasion at a fine men's apparel shop. Peruse a variety of clothing designed to outfit today's working woman. Pick up a cuddly doll for a youngster at home!

Writer Square has the new and unusual... the wonderful and enchanting! Virtually every kitchen knick-knack and cooking tool imaginable can be found. If you're searching for that fine silver service or antique vase you've dreamed of, Writer Square is the place to begin! Discover greeting cards for any occasion... wall hangings and pottery to add an international flair to your home. Convenient travel planning and banking services are here, too.

Especially important, Writer Square is easily accessible from Interstate 25 and Speer Blvd., and features plenty of convenient underground parking.

Writer Square. A special place to spend your day.

RE/MAX
REALTORS®

WOOD BROS. HOMES

For further information:
Building 12, Lakeside Lane
Denver, Colorado 80212
458-8448

Anyone doing business for over thirty years must be doing something right. There must be some secret, a guiding principle, a philosophy.

At Wood Bros. Homes, that principle is really quite simple: They built their first homes in 1950, and they've never forgotten why they build or who their customers are.

Wood Bros. homes are designed to fit the needs, attitudes, and lifestyles of the American family. They fit the family budget as well, starting from the low $40s through the luxury homes in the low $100s. Strong emphasis has always been placed in locating Wood Bros. communities in attractive areas with good schools, and in high-quality natural environments.

With over 60 different styles, in eight major home series, Wood Bros. offers an enormous range of floor plans, options, and extras. Whatever your choice — traditional, modern, ranch, two-story, tri-level, condominium, or townhome — you're sure to find something perfect for you in one of eleven distinctive communities.

Of special interest is Wood Bros. Color Center. A trained staff of consultants is made available to help you personalize your new home. The Color Center is expert at helping choose draperies, tile, cabinets, and interior and exterior color schemes.

Experienced consultants will work with you from a display of over 250 carpets, scores of linoleum, wood, and ceramic flooring samples, a complete window-covering department, cabinets, counter tops, appliances — everything needed to choose your interior and exterior decor.

Remember, it's your home. For more than three decades Wood Bros. Homes hasn't forgotten it.

THE HILLS REALTY

Garrett Bromfield

6500 E. Hampden Ave.
758-1201

It is often said that Garrett-Bromfield has a "sixth sense" about matching home buyer and home. But there is nothing mystical about their success. It is founded on a half century of dependable service to Coloradans.

That service is based on the philosophy that integrity and excellence is good for both company and client. Says Garrett-Bromfield president C.G. Cozart, "Our enthusiasm for professional performance and our attention to detail result in satisfaction for both seller and buyer."

While serving all of the Denver area, Garrett-Bromfield specializes in the central, southeast, and south suburban areas, which include such distinctive residential neighborhoods as Crestmoor Park, Cherry Hills, Southern Hills and Southmoor Park. A member of the Multiple Listing Service, they are well equipped to help you in these areas because their sales associates live and work there. They know first-hand about the schools, shopping centers, recreation facilities, transportation, churches, and the other essentials of a neighborhood.

When Garrett-Bromfield started business in Denver in 1929, they recognized the potential for development of Denver's southeast side. Like any great real estate firm, especially one that's independent and locally owned, Garrett-Bromfield was more than a broker. They helped define and develop many of these fine neighborhoods.

If you're moving to the Denver area, Garrett-Bromfield offers its excellent Home Search System, an easy, efficient way to evaluate your specific home requirements and financing, schedule your personal inspections, and match you to the home of your dreams. If you're moving away, their special relocation service links you, free of charge, to their affiliate realtor in that area, providing you with information about the types of homes available, costs, and neighborhood characteristics.

Buying and selling a home is a major undertaking for any family. At Garrett-Bromfield they understand that. "Our people are dedicated to giving the best personal service available," says president Cozart. "After all, getting *your* business is what makes *our* business possible."

Interiors

The finest in Oriental rugs and objets d'art, kitchens for gourmet cooks, beds for kids and beds that disappear, exquisite furniture, and the best in interior decorating advice are some of what you'll discover in this section.

In the midst of rapid, tumultuous change, Denver's churches stand as bulwarks of reassuring immutability. Many of the area's churches are among the oldest existing structures in the city; several are designated as historic landmarks. ✺ One such church is the Basilica of the Immaculate Conception at Logan and East Colfax—"The pinnacled glory of the West." A masterpiece of architecture, the Basilica's twin-spired facade rises with dignity and reassurance, above East Colfax. Dedicated in 1912, the Cathedral (it was designated a Basilica by Pope John Paul II in 1979) was built of limestone and granite in a pure French Gothic style reminiscent of the famous medieval European cathedrals. ✺ To glimpse the inspiring interior, you can visit the church daily from 6 a.m. to 6 p.m. The beautiful main and side altars were carved from marble quarried in Carrara, Italy. The arches and columns are pleasingly harmonious. But the masses of stained glass windows with their almost lifelike figures are the Basilica's most striking features. Made in 1900, and doubtless the ne plus ultra of Denver's stained glass art, these windows could not be duplicated today. ✺ The Basilica's forerunner, St. Mary's Church, was the second church erected in pioneer Denver, in 1860; the first was put up two months earlier by Methodists. Establishing territorial churches in a rambunctious town like Denver was certainly a test of faith. Many early churches met in log cabins and saloons, competing with gambling, fighting, and other worldly pursuits. But they persevered, bringing civilization to Denver in the form of lending libraries, hospitals, schools, and culture. ✺ Many of our city's fixtures were established by these religious pioneers—among them Denver University, Colorado School of Mines, St. Luke's and National Jewish hospitals, and Loretto Heights College. Church and private charities were also very active in aiding Denver's poor and distressed. In 1887 they formed an umbrella group that evolved into the organization most responsible today for private charitable contributions: The United Way.

INTERIOR

Residential Showrooms
3007 E. 2nd Ave.
Cherry Creek North
355-2018
599-0468

Also in Colorado Springs
at Erindale Square

Hours: Mon.-Sat. 10 am-6 pm

Home consultation by appointment

Interior Systems offers contemporary elegance in two showrooms devoted primarily to residential furniture. These feature handcrafted oak or walnut furniture and wall systems, as well as beautifully styled upholstered furniture.

Exclusivity is evident in the complete line of oak or walnut furniture by California Design Group, made and signed by individual artists. Another exclusive is a versatile line of wall systems by Richmark — sturdy wall-mounted components in a wide variety of woods and colors.

Interior Systems also offers a choice of fully upholstered sofas, loveseats, chairs, sectionals and sleepers by Schnadig, Directional, Burris and Bauhaus Canada. Take a look at lamps, wall hangings, carpets, wall and window treatments to complete your investment in quality furniture and accessories for your home.

Talk to experienced designers, at no cost or obligation, about your needs. Treat yourself to a visit to one of their inviting showrooms.

SYSTEMS

Commercial Office Showroom
3005 S. Parker Rd.
Marketplace Center
751-9830

Hours: Mon.-Fri. 8:30 am-6 pm
Saturday 10 am-6 pm

Office consultation by appointment

If you like contemporary oak and walnut office furniture, you'll love Interior Systems. They display the exclusive California Design Group line of handcrafted desks, credenzas, conference tables, chairs and files. Complete office lines also are available from Craftsman, Anderson, Myrtle and Parcwood; chair lines from Madison, Alba, Hag and Myrtle; and complementary accesso-

ries, carpets, wall coverings and window treatments. Many other popular lines also are available by catalogue.

You must see the versatile line of wall systems by Richmark — sturdy wall-mounted office components in oak, walnut and other woods. These systems can be arranged in countless configurations to get the maximum and most efficient use of your space. You can even add to or move it as the need arises.

Interior Systems' new commercial office showroom is conveniently located and allows you to choose your office furniture in a relaxed atmosphere. The staff of qualified and experienced space planners can assist you with your complete office layout — from executive desks to ashtrays.

HARTLEY HOUSE INTERIORS, LTD.

290 S. Franklin
777-0540

Hours: Mon.-Fri. 8:30-5
or by appointment

A home is not merely a place to live, but an outward expression of one's vision of life. For nearly two decades, people of vision have come to Hartley House Interiors for thoughtful guidance and inspiration in making their homes true reflections of themselves.

Hartley House designers bring a wealth of experience, creativity, and versatility to interior design. They're able to suit the most discriminating of tastes, conservative or contemporary. From snug mountain condominium to spacious urban mansion, Hartley House offers total design services. Their designers travel in an unceasing effort to unearth unique furnishings and accessories for their exclusive clientele.

James Hartley, A.S.I.D., and his professional design staff are widely known and respected throughout the West for their distinctive design. They have designed interiors across the country and as far away as Saudi Arabia. Their clients have become lifelong friends. Hartley House understands intuitively that the way one lives at home reflects the way one lives his life.

ANVILWILD
HARDWOOD FURNITURE

999 S. Logan St.
778-7770

Hours: Mon.-Sat. 9:30-5:30

Amid the forest of wood furniture manufacturers and distributors, one name stands out: Anvil Wild. Not merely because of its distinctive metallic ring, but because Anvil Wild builds the finest in solid hardwood furniture and accessories for both home and office.

Visit their showroom and see for yourself. Run your hand along the beautifully-grained, finely-finished domestic red oak, or the darker, exotic African Olive. Observe the timeless simplicity of styling, the straightforward, durable construction. Browse through the extensive line of tables, chairs, bookcases, beds, secretarial and executive desks, credenzas, display cabinets, nightstands, lamps, bars, stools, sofas and loveseats, buffets, and a variety of accessories.

It is easy to see that Anvil Wild has put craftsmanship back into wood furniture. They are not a mass production factory but a modern, well-equipped workshop where time and skill are synonymous with quality. Their origins as metal furniture makers bring several advantages to their wood construction, including precision tolerances, clean lines, tight joints, and smooth mechanical movements. Unlike furniture shipped from more humid areas, Anvil Wild's kiln-dried hardwood is acclimated to Colorado, insuring greater integrity of the joints and durability of the finished product. And their furniture is made from *solid hardwood*, not merely solid wood or hardwood veneer.

Their workshop also allows both custom designing and options in their business and home lines. And their dual role as manufacturer and distributor keeps their costs competitive. No middleman and transportation mark-ups here.

Once you visit, you'll understand why amid a wilderness of discounts, sales, and cheap imitations, Anvil Wild has built its reputation by not compromising quality for cost. You will find less expensive furniture elsewhere, but you won't find a better value for your dollar anywhere.

Howard Lorton Galleries

1155 Lincoln
831-1212

Free delivery available

A spectacular three-story brick building of curves and arches on 12th Avenue from Broadway to Lincoln is the new home of Howard Lorton Galleries.

It graces the fringe of the burgeoning downtown area and is quite unlike any of the new Denver structures. Designed by Callister, Gately and Bischoff of Tiburan, California, it is the keystone of a complex that brings together all Lorton facilities and provides a showcase for a selection of fine home furnishings unsurpassed in this country.

When Howard Lorton built the original store on Speer Boulevard, it was an innovative gesture for a businessman of the 1920s. The land-filled property, once a city dump, was considered "out in the country." It was the first store in the region to include an interior designer on the staff.

Howard Lorton came to Colorado in 1908 from Roodhouse, Illinois. He first entered the camera business and then began a career in furniture merchandising at the Denver Dry Goods Company. When he opened his own establishment in 1927, his philosophy was to utilize the best sources in the home furnishing field and to provide a very personal service to his customers. The tradition continues under the guidance of his grandson, William Lorton Cook, who now serves as president. Lois Lorton, daughter of the founder, is vice-president. Howard Lorton and Robert Kuykendall, an accomplished designer, were the only members of the firm when it was founded in 1927. Today, there are fifty employees with twenty designers.

The precarious days following the stock market crash of 1929 and shortages during World War II were followed by a prospering period of growth. Expansions in 1947 and 1962 more than tripled the floor space. When Cook took over as president, following the death of his grandfather in 1960, growth continued at a quickening pace. A new Lorton store was opened in 1979 in Colorado Springs. In March, 1982, the Springs store moved into greatly expanded quarters in the heart of the downtown area.

Lorton's new Denver store on 12th Avenue brings display areas, administrative and design offices, drapery and upholstery workrooms and warehouses together. Spacious galleries and showrooms are filled with fine furniture: names like Baker, Henredon, John Widdicomb, Statton, Kindel, Conant Ball, Hickory Chair, Hekman. There are lamps from Wildwood, Chapman, Marbro, Frederick Cooper, Stiffel, carpets and rugs from Karastan and Customweave, fabrics from Schumacher and Brunschwig & Fils, patio furniture from Woodard, Brown Jordan and Tropitone. Lorton's design service, known throughout the Rocky Mountain West for its excellence, is provided without charge with purchase.

ROCHE-BOBOIS

**3045 S. Parker Rd.
Aurora, CO 80014
751-5444**

**Open daily 10 a.m.-6 p.m.
Thursdays until 9**

Color Catalogue — 140 pages At Store or by Mail, $6

Roche-Bobois is a world of uncompromising elegance.

That's worth another thought, so take a moment. Consider the word.

Elegance. Refinement and grace. Unbridled luxury in superior European furnishings. Good taste and polish beyond compare. Beauty beyond the orthodox. Rhythm, symmetry and harmony beyond doubt.

Elegance. A classic-contemporary home environment. At Roche-Bobois it all begins with service. Customers, old favorites or first-timers, are greeted with the same elegant welcome. Inside, an expert staff guides you, adds luster to your own fine ideas, challenges, helps define and refine them, all with the big goal of creating that contemporary environment perfectly suited to your standards.

Going hand-in-hand with elegance is originality. Roche-Bobois carries a wide range of exceptional articles, international in scope, and—with very few exceptions—exclusive to Roche-Bobois. Each item bearing the Roche-Bobois name has been sought out or designed in select cities around the world.

The store itself is a genuine original. Here are selections for the young, for designers, for final touches. You could buy Roche-Bobois items in their stores in Paris or New York, but the only store in the Rocky Mountain region is in Denver, at Market Place Center on Parker Road. People come from five states to peruse the collection, proving the contention of Roche-Bobois president Will Glowacki that "We're more than just a fine top-end European furniture store. Our furniture creates an ambience."

"Roche-Bobois is committed to elegance, before, during and after the sale. If you have a problem at any stage of our business together, we will solve it." That's an attitude that some people believe belongs to another, more elegant and special, era.

At Roche-Bobois, the era is now.

693 E. Speer Blvd.
733-2623

Hours: by appointment

Sarkisian's
Oriental Rugs and Fine Arts

When you venture into the vast, complex world of Asian art, it's prudent to have a seasoned, knowledgeable guide. Denver is home to one of the most highly respected collections in the country . . . Sarkisian's Oriental Rugs and Fine Arts.

H. Medill Sarkisian's travel in Asia spans half a century. Although he views himself as simply a student, his lifelong study has brought recognition to Sarkisian as an expert in Asian art and a foremost authority on Asian textiles. To others, Sarkisian is a 20th century renaissance man, steeped in Asian geography, political history, geology, art history, language and rug-making.

A deep sense of history is reflected in the quality of the collection of fine rugs and priceless art displayed in his showroom. A collection of the finest modern rugs available in the market today is also available. An exclusive feature of Sarkisian's is their ability to custom design and hand tie contemporary rugs for their clientele.

"I have a tendency to swim against the commercial tide," explains Sarkisian. "Quality is the most important part of my establishment. I have always looked for the best, knowing that it may be years, if ever, before we find the right collector."

Sarkisian's business has been in the family for three generations. The showroom rivals the quality of many of the finest museums in the country.

For the serious collector, a visit by appointment at Sarkisian's will lead into a fascinating world of cultural richness. The exquisite collection of rugs, dating from the 17th century, includes pieces originating in Turkey, the Caucasus, Persia, China, and India. Asian art includes Persian ceramic water vessels of the 11th century B.C., 7th-9th century T'ang Dynasty ceramics, a 10th century gilded wood Buddha, a 17th century Japanese suit of armor, and countless other precious antiques.

Through his showroom or in person, Sarkisian is a man who believes passionately in sharing his knowledge of Asia with others. He plans to donate much of his collection, spanning 4,000 years and embracing all of Asia, to his alma mater, the University of Colorado. In the meantime, the impressive sweep of Asian history and art at Sarkisian's remains an inspirational experience for the Asian collector.

Interior Reflections

1961 Wazee Street
Suite 300 E
595-0401

An interior designer must have two major assets: creativity and an ability to visualize the client's desires, visions, and needs.

Interior Reflections excels at both. Owner/designer Linda Hanson treats her clients as friends, taking the time to thoroughly understand their wants and needs for creating a comfortable, exciting interior environment. She has a special sensitivity for families and their needs, for she has children of her own.

Her clients appreciate this, and they've recommended her strongly to others. Though Interior Reflections is located in Denver, Linda has designed interiors for numerous private residences, condominiums, and commercial offices in various Colorado mountain communities. She even has clients as far away as Texas, California, Florida, Mexico and Venezuela.

Linda prefers to create interiors from the ground up. She pays careful attention to detail, working with blueprints and consulting with architects. Her tastes run from traditional to contemporary, with a style frequently concentrating on earth tones accented boldly.

Linda brings years of experience to interior design. She is a consultant for New Home Marketing Company and its associated custom builders, and is a member of the Homebuilders Association and Sales Marketing Council, which keeps her abreast of the economic and building trends in Colorado.

The successful blending of old and new architecture in Interior Reflections' own offices downtown reflect Linda's imaginative approach to design. Clients relax with refreshments from a delightful tile-accented bar, and browse through a showroom of window, wall, and floor coverings, and extensive fabric and furniture samples.

It is a place for easy, stimulating consultation, a place where interior visions are transformed into interior realities.

BRUCE BARTHEL

2640 E. 3rd
399-5802

Creative kitchenry.

Don't run to your dictionary. We've just invented a new word. Kitchenry—an environment conducive to wonderful foodstuffs. A state of mind where the day's nourishment begins and ends, where even potluck is approached with tender loving care.

Beautifully executed, lavishly appointed with the latest in appliances and accessories, our showroom kitchens form the heart of a store that's widely regarded as one of the premier kitchen stores in the country.

But the showroom is only a starting point, an inspirational leap to help people visualize the beauty and functionalism they desire in their own home. At Kitchens By Kline no two kitchens are ever alike. Bill Kline and his professional staff of designers and consultants see to that.

Whether remodeling, or building a new kitchen, our designers prepare a plan that best fits the individual's needs for efficiency, aesthetics, and budget. They make certain the design answers the most important question of all: Will it cook?

As kitchens increasingly become the focal point for entertainment and gourmet experimentation, the answer to that question becomes paramount.

The imaginative designs at Kitchens By Kline are flawlessly executed by skilled craftsmen installing the best appliances and the most respected names in cabinetry, names such as St. Charles and Rutt.

The design and installation is backed by three decades of creating kitchens all over the Rocky Mountain region.

This is the kind of store you'd expect to find only in New York City: the Cadillac of the kitchen business. But Bill Kline, known as Denver's "Mr. Kitchen," loves Colorado.

And Coloradans love Kitchens by Kline.

KITCHENS BY KLINE
A COLORADO CORPORATION

Arvada Hardwood Floor Co.

11095 E. 45th Ave.
373-0350

Flooring is not just something under-foot. Often it's the most visible element in a room, establishing the mood, pull-ing together—or tearing apart—every-thing else. People who demand the very best go to Arvada Hardwood Floor.

For two decades, President Harold "Willie" Northrup has installed the best flooring in town. He specializes in hardwood floors for residential and commercial customers. He has earned an impeccable reputation for craftsman-ship, service, and dependability.

As the most established hardwood floor company in the region, Arvada Hardwood has done a great deal of custom work, including the flooring for the finest athletic clubs around.

Nothing compares to the natural beau-ty and elegance of hardwood. It is long-lasting, durable, easy to maintain, and timeless in its subtle beauty. Its variety of design, texture, and wood can satisfy any discriminating taste, from antique to contemporary. Choose from the ever-popular traditional strip oak or rich walnut, parquet or plank, herringbone or louvre. The possibilities are many.

Arvada Hardwood carries such top lines as Kentucky Wood Floors, Harris, and Bruce Hardwood Floors. They also offer a wide range for your budget, from low-cost, non-custom flooring to the finest on-the-job custom work, installed to exacting tolerances.

Along with hardwood flooring, Arvada Hardwood installs carpeting, tile, and drapes. And they offer sound interior design advice to tie everything together.

So don't walk on just any old floor. Walk on the finest: an Arvada Hardwood Floor.

SHAVER-RAMSEY

2414 E. 3rd Ave.
320-6363

Amid the provincialism and enticement of the Cherry Creek North shopping area there exists an oasis of cultural timelessness. Shaver-Ramsey Galleries has been offering distinctive Asian artifacts for five years at that location, and during that time Carolyn Shaver and Paul Ramsey have established an outstanding international reputation.

From the outside, the Gallery appears to be of modest proportions though various in its offerings. Once inside, one learns that there are four levels displaying everything from a Chinese wedding bed and Japanese kimonos through Ming vases and Korean money chests.

But the main emphasis of this business is rugs. And do they have rugs! There are rugs ranging in size from one foot by two feet all the way up to 15 feet by 20 feet and ranging in age from 10 years to 150 years. Prices also vary greatly.

Mr. Ramsey was kind enough to explain that most all of their rugs are made from hand-spun, hand-dyed and hand-woven wool and can reasonably anticipate a useful life in excess of 50 years. These rugs originate from Persia, Turkey, Afghanistan and the southern extremes of Russia.

We also learned that aside from the usual pile rugs that we associate with the Middle East, there is another breed known as the *kilim* or flat-woven rug. These pieces are rapidly becoming favorites with interior designers all over the country and are available at Shaver-Ramsey in an eye-stopping profusion of colors.

So come by 2414 East Third Avenue the next time you're in the neighborhood and ask any of the friendly and knowledgeable staff for a tour.

Hillary Reed Interiors

2575 W. Main St.
Littleton
755-5945

Colorado's Hillary Reed is known as one of the most resourceful young designers in a most competitive field. Her diversity in developing interior themes and decorative schemes makes enhancing architecture an easy assignment—from simple to dramatic.

After careful research of the specific market segment, Hillary designs for the emotional appeal of the prospective buyer. What she creates with color, texture, accessories, special treatments and a touch of romance establishes a memorable, livable home and buyer-rapport.

Her experience and reputation for designing model homes and sales offices speaks for itself . . . The Writer Corporation, Medema Homes, Sebring Properties, MD Properties, Ltd., Tridel, Heritage Financial Corporation, McStain Enterprises-Boulder, R&S Construction-Colorado Springs, Keating Homes-Seattle, and more.

Hillary's formula and philosophy of the art of merchandising for home builders is to maintain the balance and harmony of function and creativity. The functional aspect of the environment—realism and affordability with fantasy—emotionally-packed future expectations, lifestyle and fun!

A tour of her projects reveals her ability to communicate through aesthetics. The reflection is Hillary—warmth, individuality, distinction, comfort, sophistication and freshness. The feeling is that of enchantment—from country to contemporary, from oriental to Southwestern.

Hillary's exquisite taste and professionalism have led to invitations to design for the ASID Showhouse in Central City and the Denver Symphony Showhouse.

Her range of capabilities is not limited to model homes, but includes private residences, commercial and retail spaces and clubs. Her signature is quiet elegance. In essence—the only designer one would ever need.

Her professional credentials include the prestigious ASID designation and active participation in the Homebuilders Association of Metropolitan Denver and its sales and marketing council. She is a recipient of the council's coveted MAME award (Major Achievement in Merchandising Excellence) for interior design.

Scandinavian Design ⏎

3242 E. Colfax
355-0201

Oriental rugs are like exotic languages reflecting artistic, cultural, and historical traditions spanning thousands of years.

At Oriental Rug Gallery Ltd. they'll put this woven heritage at your feet, with select offerings of Chinese, Persian and other oriental rugs—new, semi-antique, antique. These are rugs of sound investment: masterpieces of the knotted art.

Oriental Rug Gallery receives new shipments every day from the continental markets of London to Peking, making theirs an ever-changing, incomparable selection.

If you aren't familiar with the exquisite beauty and the financial reliability of these pieces of floor artistry, owner Martin Wirth will gladly offer you a glass of wine and spend some time informing you. Amidst the fragrance of a Bagdad bazaar, you'll quickly be caught up in his enthusiasm. Martin grew up in the rug business, spent years in the Orient, and has an impeccable reputation for his knowledge and his candid approach to rug selling.

Martin works closely with designers and others in the trade, and he offers excellent investment guidance to corporations interested in purchasing fine carpets.

PAPAZIAN

The Oriental Rug Gallery is a member of the select Oriental Rug Retailers Association. The gallery has an excellent reference library, and can restore, appraise and clean your rugs.

If you're searching for something special, the gallery will do the legwork to find it, wherever it may be.

The Oriental Rug Gallery will be bringing in collections and exhibitions in the future. A rug leasing line is also being developed.

Martin's infectious enthusiasm for this fine art is taking him on the lecture circuit where he can spread his knowledge and experience. Once you've seen these rare and elegant rugs at Oriental Rug Gallery, you'll be caught up too in his enthusiasm.

ORIENTAL RUG GALLERY

contemporary showcase ltd.

3186 S. Parker Road
755-3411

"Interior Jewelry" is how Terry Brumfiel describes his exceptional lines of contemporary furniture, lamps, and accessories at Contemporary Showcase. You'll find the timeless elegance and the beauty of European styling at Contemporary Showcase and much more than that.

When you visit their showroom, you'll view some of the most appealing interior settings that can be found in the Denver area. The beautifully displayed rooms will excite one's interior decorating imagination.

If you like the sparkle of glass, the gleam of chrome and brass, and sculptured accessories, visit Contemporary Showcase.

Many ideas come to mind as you look at the large selection of home furnishings in the most current fabrics, fine woods, and finishes including high glass and lacquer finishes.

To help turn your decorating fantasies into reality, Contemporary Showcase offers complimentary interior design services, with an unlimited world of fabric and drapery coordination to choose from.

Contemporary Showcase is conveniently located immediately west of I-225 on Parker Road in the Regatta Plaza Shopping Center.

EAST INDIA COMPANY

Cherry Creek North
2829 E. Third Ave.
322-9294

Hours: Mon.-Sat. 10-5

Browsing at the East India Company is like touring the exotic side of the world. Where else in Denver can you find such items as Buddhist prayer book pages, a Japanese Tansus, hand-carved and hand-decorated crafts from Bali, and a bamboo nautical instrument from the Marshall Islands?

Owners and treasure seekers Toni Lorie and David Yeakley have created a shop as unusual as its merchandise. They specialize primarily in decorative arts from the Far East—Indonesia to Korea to Mainland China—though they do have unique items from Europe, primitive arts from New Guinea and Africa, and finds from the New World. Some pieces are fine antiques, but many are for a modest budget. Everything is authentic, and most often, one-of-a-kind. Each piece is selected during trips to faraway and often remote parts of the world.

These offerings are displayed in their Cherry Creek North shop in an atmosphere as quiet and contemplative as the interior of an exotic temple. Once you've visited the East India Company you'll go back. Its world is never the same.

PLAYNIX, INC.

1004 S. Gaylord
744-8406

345 E. Jefferson Ave.
Englewood
761-5630

Lake Arbor Shopping Center
7531 W. 80th
Arvada
420-TOYS

Getting a child to bed is one of the exasperating duties of parenthood. But with children's furniture from Playnix, getting your child *away* from bed may become the challenge.

What child could resist a crib that looks like a lion, a bed built like a railroad engine, or a bunk bed that doubles as a clubhouse with a tree tower and slide?

These and many more unique, custom designed children's furniture items, along with a fine assortment of sturdy educational toys, fill one of the most creative children's stores you'll find anywhere.

Playnix is the creation of Fred and Diane Hale, whose furniture needs for their five children turned from a personal necessity into a regionally recognized business.

The furniture, featuring 80 different designs, smoothly combines necessity and whimsy. It's safe and sturdy, non-tiltable, and has rounded corners and kid-proof stops on drawers. It is available painted or unpainted. Many parents have found great enjoyment in putting on their own decorations.

The furniture also is an excellent investment, often selling for more than the original purchase price.

Playnix has furniture and toys for children of all ages, including a contemporary line for teenagers. They carry an especially strong selection of European toys, which serve to stimulate and subtly teach the child while playing.

This imaginative furniture, complemented by the interior design talents of Fred and Diane Hale, has found its way into physicians' offices, nurseries, libraries, day care centers, clinics, and many area hospitals.

Your children will love finding their way through Playnix's three stores. They're happy places, with kids exploring the bright, vivid furniture and toys. If you lose track of your kids you'll probably find them playing—or sleeping—in the stagecoach bunk bed, or the doll house, or the fire truck, or the . . .

1961 Wazee
623-8429

Hours: Mon.-Sat. 10-5
Appointment in home for consultation

"You give us one room . . . We'll give you two."

Now there's an offer that's tough to refuse. And people are finding it impossible to refuse Wall Beds Unlimited once they've seen these space-saving beds and furniture.

Need a bed to disappear in the morning? Want the bedroom to become a sewing room or a playroom for the kids? Or a bed to magically appear in the family room to sleep over guests or family? Wall Beds can do the trick.

Wall Beds is the exclusive Rocky Mountain area distributor for the SICO Room Maker bed. They specialize in space-saving furniture such as kitchen tables or desks that conveniently fold out of the way. The beds need only 18 inches of wall space in which to disappear, giving you the equivalent of a whole new room. At a time when remodeling means refinancing, when heating extra bedrooms stretches and breaks budgets, when condominiums and townhouses are priced by the square inch, that multiple use of space can mean huge savings and convenience.

If your back aches from just the memory of those old thin-mattress Murphys or sofa beds, try out a Wall Bed. These beds, available in any size, come with regular box springs and mattress and are as comfortable as anything you'll find. Your head remains completely outside the wall recess while you sleep, and the ingeniously slanted headrest cradles you for TV viewing or reading while cradling the pillows during storage. The entire bed raises or lowers with the touch of a finger. And the beds are maintenance-free and durable.

The beds come in a variety of attractive storage units, including shelving, in-the-wall night stand, and folding desk. Wall Beds Unlimited can also design custom cabinetry for your particular needs, decor, and living space.

Irresistible? Visit Wall Beds Unlimited's showroom. Give them 18 inches . . . and they'll give you a bedroom.

Shopping & Business Districts

What's more fun than shopping, and what's more convenient than shopping districts? From exclusive one-of-a-kind boutiques to major department stores, from the excitement of the new 16th Street Mall to the unhurried pace of a delightful square—match your mood to our listings and you can't miss.

The Sakura (cherry blossom) Festival is a tradition in Japan, a springtime tribute to nature's beauty and constant renewal. Thus it was appropriate that the completion of Sakura Square in 1972, covering an entire city block around 19th, 20th, Lawrence and Larimer, marked the first completed portion of Denver's ambitious Skyline Urban Renewal project, conceived to revitalize a deteriorated section of downtown. ⚘ Developed by the members of the Tri-State Buddhist Temple, the complex of shops, markets, restaurants, and a 20-story apartment building is dedicated to the memory of "the men and women of Japanese ancestry who brought oriental art, religion, and culture to the Rocky Mountains, and to those who continue to sustain and cherish this heritage." ⚘ Whether you visit Sakura Square to shop or to sightsee, it is a lovely, tranquil place, a respite from the harried pace of the city. The buildings are surrounded by sculptured Japanese gardens, and of special beauty is the courtyard garden of the Temple, located on the northeast corner of the Square. Behind an attractive wooden wall in the courtyard is a tile-roofed belltower housing a 1½-ton ornamented bronze "bonsho" temple bell. ⚘ In late May or early June (the cherry blossoms bloom later here) the Square holds its own Sakura Festival. All residents and visitors are welcome to participate in the variety of cultural arts, crafts, music, dancing, athletic competition, and food. ⚘ It is a perfect opportunity to see the dramatic changes downtown—and for the West to meet the East.

7777 E. Hampden Ave.

**Convenience Center, around corner
3333 S. Tamarac**

Shopping should be a tranquil, intimate experience. A time to browse at your leisure. A time to escape the pressures of everyday life.

Tamarac Square provides that experience. Elegance, intimacy, and thoughtful consideration of the shopper make this an oasis of restaurants, one-of-a-kind shops, and theaters.

Two levels of stores are set around an old English street scene. Skylights illumine the paved interior courtyard. Full-size trees canopy over comfortable benches. A feeling of the outdoors pervades without the vagaries of weather.

Although intimate and casual, Tamarac Square is larger than it appears. More than 60 specialty shops, 6 theaters, and 7 select restaurants captivate

the shopper. They handle everything from shoes to fancy luggage, blue jeans to evening wear, ice cream to quiche Lorraine. Many shops carry items not found anywhere else in the Rocky Mountain region.

There's ample parking, accessible to both levels, and the Square is conveniently located one mile east of I-25 and Hampden Avenue.

At Tamarac Square, you'll discover just how rewarding shopping can be.

TAMARAC SQUARE

Marina Square

**8101 East Belleview Ave. at
The Denver Technological Center**

Mon.-Sat. 10 a.m.-6 p.m.

Shopping becomes a pleasurable experience at the more than three dozen shops within Marina Square Shopping Center located one block east of I-25 on Belleview Avenue near the Denver Technological Center.

Designed, developed and constructed by Loup-Miller, shops open onto a landscaped courtyard, with its own pond and streams. There's an unhurried feeling here; then, the immediate sense that there's no need to elbow.

Many of the merchants are owner-managers who give immediate personal service that's become all too rare.

There are places to rest and refresh—perhaps at Singer's or Marina Landing. Paul's Place, Le Petite Cafe and The Filet entice with fresh bakery items, and quality fish and meats. Indulge your sweet tooth at Blum's Of San Francisco. Find more than a health food store at The Natural Alternative.

There's International Villa, known for silver, china, crystal and jewelry on everyone's most-wanted list.

Prominent at Marina Square are retailers long-recognized as quality clothiers for women, men and children . . . Montaldo's . . . Homer Reed . . . Merry Simmons.

Women's fashions embody panache and tradition at Eugenie Ann, Le Cadeau Boutique, Elizabeth Woods, The Limited, The Country Pacer, Tandem, Pappagallo's or Jack Gleason's Casual Shop.

There's more men's wear at Man's World.

Look for a new look at Niko's Cosmetics or Inter-Hair with eyewear from New Concept Optical.

Browse for a book at Books Et Cetera II. Drop a line on William Ernest Brown stationery.

Bed, bath and home furnishers abound: Chrome Concepts, Marina Bed & Bath, Villa Too, European Sleep Shop and A La Table.

Find those other specialties. Shoes from Senatore's II, sportswear from Phidippides, the essentials from Denver Dance, children's playthings from The Toy Place, art work at Gallery I, flowers from the Marina Square flower shop and even dependable cleaning from Dependable Cleaners.

Marina Square. It's synonymous with variety, quality and leisurely shopping.

Simply one of the nicest places to search for something special.

DENVER PARTNERSHIP

From sunup to sundown, and into the night, the quickening pace of this city is felt. No longer is it merely the "Gateway to the Rockies"; it has emerged as the recognized center of commerce of a multi-state region — an area rich in resources, and richer still in the quality of its life.

But, while metropolitan Denver experiences a "coming of age," perhaps to an extent undreamed of only a few years ago, its central core district is challenged by a new era of rebirth and revitalization.

It is here—in the area known as "downtown" — that enormous change is taking place. Newcomers and natives alike are daily witnesses to the rising skyline, the increasing complexity of fitting the new Denver together. As the economic, cultural, political and social heart of the new west, downtown Denver faces perhaps the most significant city building challenges in America today. How well the individual and collective private sector responds — in cooperation with public interests — will determine the shape of this city for the rest of the century.

Understanding the premise that Colorado's and Denver's greatest growth lies ahead, Downtown Denver has embarked upon an ambitious program to create the public-private partnerships necessary to stimulate and guide the central city's revitalization.

An "umbrella" center city organization known as "Denver Partnership" has been incorporated. Denver Partnership includes two operating corporations: Downtown Denver, Inc., respected as one of the country's oldest downtown business organizations, and a new corporation, Denver Civic Ventures.

The highly visible Downtown Denver, Inc. will continue to play an activist role in directing existing business and community energies toward effective management, operation and promotion of downtown.

Through Denver Civic Ventures, public-private partnerships are being established to coordinate special purpose planning, urban design, financial packaging, and development capabilities. Civic Ventures seeks to serve foundations and corporations in their contributions to center city revitalizations.

Denver today is a city vibrant with success—confident of its future—in love with its image. With care, vision and leadership . . . it can indeed become one of America's truly great urban centers.

LARIMER SQUARE

**1400 block of Larimer
534-2367**

Larimer Square is a state of mind. Just walking down the 1400 block of Larimer Street captures the spirit of Denver's past and the promise of its future.

The handsome Victorian buildings lend a sense of history and vitality to every shopping and dining experience. Strolling through the restored porticos and lanes opens a world of exotic perfumes, elegant dance halls, fancy ladies in stiff silks and jaunty men in derby hats. The arcades of Larimer Square hint at back rooms and bars, where Colorado's first legislators quenched their thirsts and made decisions that would affect the West for a century to come.

Denver's most historic block is the place to find unusual wares and wearables, from the chic and sophisticated to the comfortable look of the '80s.

For the body, there's fine leather clothing, exclusive lingerie, high-fashion footwear, custom-tailored men's shirts, imaginative children's apparel, European clothing and accessories, imported folkware, jewelry and artifacts of new, antique and American Indian origins.

For the soul, Larimer Square offers a vast array of books, colorful prints, needlework supplies and classes, rich sweets, pastries and sinful chocolates, copper and brassware, foreign and classic films, a complete wine boutique, a year'round Country Christmas Store, hand made kites, scents and cosmetics,

imported crystal and foods from around the world.

The renowned restaurants of Larimer Square offer the gourmet options ranging from Cajun Creole to subtle Continental; from a burger and beer to hearty Italian fare. There are spicy dishes from south of the border, elaborate ice cream concoctions, Belgian waffles and scrumptious salads. Whatever your palate fancies, it's here in Larimer Square.

Night life includes two cabarets, a comedy workshop and live blues, jazz and rock bands.

An hour or an evening spent in Larimer Square provides you with an entree into a world gone by. Let your whims meet your fancies in this neighborhood of legends.

CHERRY CREEK NORTH

What is today known as Cherry Creek North was little more than a cluster of buildings when the growing city of Denver annexed the area in 1894. Those buildings included a livery stable and a general store, the last stage stop where salesmen would refresh themselves before making their calls in Denver. Not long after the turn of the century, however, the area around what is now University Boulevard and First Avenue became one of the city's most fashionable neighborhoods. A few mom-and-pop stores served those who chose not to shop downtown, and so the situation remained for many years.

But when developer Temple Buell built Cherry Creek Shopping Center in the 1950s, the area north of First Avenue and east of University started changing. An increasing number of fascinating shops opened, offering an array of products and services. The district developed its own identity, came to be called Cherry Creek North, and gained a reputation for the many off-beat quality establishments located there. This prestige has accelerated in the past five years, until today, Cherry Creek North has by far the most comprehensive collection of unusual shops and restaurants to be found in Denver.

Almost 150 establishments, most operated by their owners, can today be found in Cherry Creek North. The assortment of shops include fashion clothing stores for men and women, art galleries, furniture galleries, bakeries, bookstores and cardshops, jewelry stores, imported gift shops, shoe stores, audio equipment stores, and many more. There are such special services as interior design studios, custom frame shops, beauty salons and barber shops, photographers, opticians, and banks.

Cherry Creek North is noted for its many restaurants, from fast food outlets to elegant restaurants serving continental or even Vietnamese cuisine. In addition, many professionals have their offices in the area—doctors, lawyers, accountants, and graphic designers among them.

One can walk leisurely down Second or Third Avenues window shopping, running into friends along the way. The annual Third Avenue sidewalk sale in August always features remarkable bargains and many entertaining sights. The district is easily reached from anywhere in the city and parking spaces are always available.

Roger Cawthon, a business owner in Cherry Creek North, says the area is now gaining many new shops as construction proceeds on several buildings. "Cherry Creek North is a quality shopping area," he says. "We have anything a discriminating shopper may desire."

AURORA MALL

**14200 E. Alameda, I-225 at Alameda
344-4120**

Aurora Mall has made shopping fun again!

"There's always something going on at Aurora Mall," says Frank Loner, president of the Aurora Mall Merchant Association. "Today's shopper is looking for more in a shopping center than just good values and excellent quality, so we're making sure that our customers associate Aurora Mall with fun and entertainment."

This effort is summed up in "Emphasis: Entertainment '82," an assortment of events scheduled year 'round at Aurora Mall. What kinds of events? You name it.

Last April, for example, patrons at the Mall were greeted by Harvey, the six foot tall invisible white rabbit (a Pookah, actually) made famous in the play

"Harvey" by Denver's own Mary Chase. Harvey arrived on a Saturday morning in a chauffeured limousine, escorted by a visible human, and then proceeded to the Mall's center court where he posed for pictures with children and the young at heart. Harvey then judged an "invisible pet" show at noon, with the winning child receiving $100 cash.

Other special events this year have included an appearance by Susan from "Sesame Street," the 1982 Bridal Fair, the Spring Home and Garden Show, and the Draw-Your-Mother contest on Mother's Day. Events planned for later this year are the Total Art Experience Show, Healthline '82, the People's Choice Awards and a "Messiah" sing-along this coming Christmas featuring the Hallelujah Chorus from Handel's uplifting work.

The most popular event of the Empha-

sis: Entertainment series is the monthly program, "Malltalk," hosted by television personality Larry Green. Using a format similar to the "Tonight Show" or "Hour Magazine," the program features interviews with interesting people on the Colorado scene, such as First Lady Dottie Lamm, Former Miss America Marilyn VanDerber, Denver Broncos, and fashion designers. Although the shows are not broadcast, audiences of 10,000 people often turn out for the show, held at 11 am in the Center Court on the third Tuesday of every month.

The entertainment is indeed a good reason to shop at Aurora Mall, but the main reasons for going there are its 136 stores from major department stores to small boutiques. Almost anything a shopper could ever need is under one roof at Aurora Mall.

Fashions & Services

Western wear. Custom shirts. Kids' toys. Photography. Furs. Intimate undergarments. Hairstyling. Jeans. Formal wear. Choosing the best in fashions and services can be bewildering. Denver Now has separated the wheat from the chaff. Just turn the page.

Denver has a solid reputation as one of America's favorite convention cities. The mild weather, the irresistible backdrop of the Front Range, and the Western hospitality have over the years lured nearly every major national convention to Denver. ✒ Currigan Exhibition Hall, dedicated in 1965, is part of a convention complex Denver has built over the years to accommodate the demand. Named for Mayor Tom Currigan, this award-winning hall provides more than 100,000 square feet of unobstructed floor space. Currigan can seat 14,000 people and display up to 600 exhibition booths. In a given month, Currigan, along with the rest of the convention complex, may host more than 100 events, from a Broadway show to a state bar exam, from religious meetings to trade exhibitions. ✒ Even in the 1880s Denver was developing its reputation as a host city by holding an annual mining and industrial exposition. In 1908, under energetic Mayor Robert Speer, the city dedicated its $500,000 Municipal Auditorium at 14th and Curtis. At the time, the Auditorium, now called the Auditorium Theatre and linked by bridge to Currigan Hall, was the second largest in America, behind only Madison Square Garden. It opened in grand style, hosting the National Democratic Convention. ✒ Denver's first, and only, national political convention focused attention on the still-isolated Queen City of the Plains. City Hall and business leaders didn't pass up the opportunity. Promotion began in earnest. Slogans like "Cool, Colorful Colorado" and "Denver, the City Beautiful" attracted more and more conventioneers and tourists. Convention facilities were expanded and added. ✒ Today, visitors are a staple of the city's economy and character, and no minor staple at that. Annually, they ring the area's cash registers to the tune of some $100 million.

Andrisen Morton Co.

Traditional Clothier

740 17th Street
623-4411

Store hours — Mon.-Fri. 9:30-5:30
                Saturday 10:00-5:00

The Andrisen Morton Company believes that fine men's clothing is meant to be selected with care, deliberation and sound advice.

That's why the staff at Andrisen Morton gives such personal attention to every customer—insuring the perfect fit and a pleasant buying experience.

At Andrisen Morton, clothing is shown in natural shoulder classic three-button models woven in natural fibers. Andrisen Morton Co. offers the best in Alden shoes, Talbott ties, Troy Guild shirts, Corbin, Burberry top coats, as well as their own private-label clothing. Hand tailoring by a full-time staff guarantees a fit of uncommon perfection.

Located in the historic Equitable Building, Andrisen Morton reveals the patina of hand-rubbed mahogany and classic wallcoverings (noticeable by their display windows which have won acclaim) and a tasteful interior which matches their clothing.

It's not surprising that Andrisen Morton has gained a national reputation. They are clothiers of distinction, with personal dedication to their customers.

1590 Court Pl.
628-0497

Hours: Mon.-Sat. 9-5:30

Jim Butcher, a unique and quality western wear store conveniently located in the heart of downtown Denver, in the Hilton Hotel, on the new 16th Street Mall, specializes in the finest apparel for both men and women of discriminating taste.

Jim Butcher offers the best in hand made boots by Lucchese, T.O. Stanley, R.J. Foley, Tony Lama and Larry Mahan, in such exotic skins as alligator, ostrich, lizard, elephant, hornback lizard, kangaroo, eel, crocodile, Anaconda, etc. . . .

If you're looking for excellent western hats, Jim Butcher has a great selection by Stetson and Biltmore. Beautiful hand-tailored suits and sport coats by Le Baron in natural fibers and year-round weights such as tropical wools, camel hair, cashmere, silks, and Ultra Suede. In leather, Jim Butcher carries stunning sport coats and vests by Scully Leatherwear.

You'll find a wide selection of gift items and accessories such as gold and silver belt buckles, silver hat bands, bolos, and money clips.

So let Jim Butcher welcome you to the store and discover that famous Western hospitality—and quality—at its best.

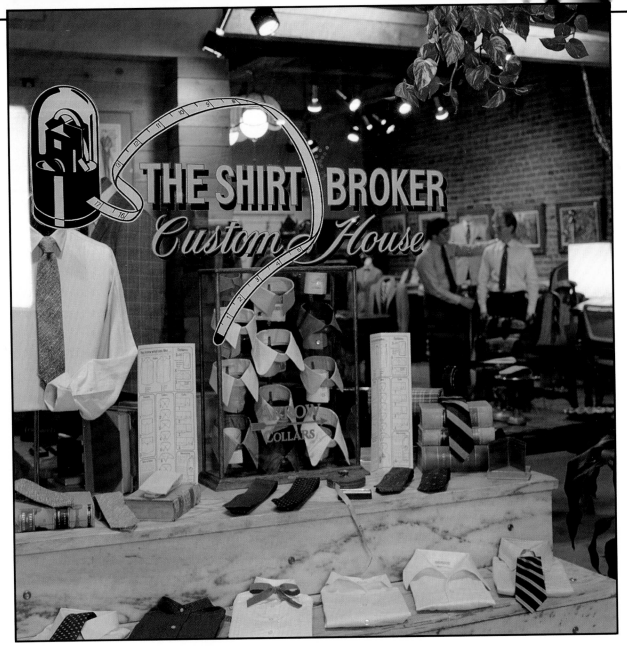

530 17th St.
572-3031

A downtown Denver tradition for more than fifteen years, The Shirt Broker is one of the few clothing firms in the United States offering custom made shirts and clothing exclusively.

Why should you consider wearing custom fitted garments? Slight variations in body dimensions can make significant impact on how clothing fits. Also, custom tailoring allows you to select the style you desire along with the fabric and color. Let the friendly, experienced staff help you with these decisions.

Custom tailored shirts and clothing from The Shirt Broker will help you look and feel more comfortable with your wardrobe.

Join the men and women who have over the years come to The Shirt Broker for their custom tailoring needs.

THE SHIRT BROKER
Custom House

THE BUCCANEER LTD.

"On the Hill" in Boulder
1310 College Ave.
444-0881

Tamarac Square
7777 E. Hampden Ave.
751-9030

Cherry Creek Square
3000 E. 3rd Ave.
320-4363

Also in Casper, WY
and Colorado Springs, CO

When The Buccaneer opened the doors of their Boulder store in 1968, the 900 square-foot store carried traditional, classic merchandise specifically to accommodate the junior-size woman. The basic philosophy of the store was to provide excellent service and quality

merchandise. Fourteen years and five stores later, The Buccaneer has diversified their merchandise and attitudes to accommodate women of all ages. Their original philosophy and classic traditional approach to women's apparel has remained and has, in fact, become their trademark.

The Buccaneer staff has maintained the lost art of courteous, creative and helpful assistance in a pleasant, relaxed atmosphere. Wardrobe planning and investment dressing coordination is available from saleswomen who understand a customer's needs and offer knowledgeable and informative direction. At The Buccaneer you can expect an individual approach to your needs.

The Buccaneer stores provide a fresh attitude and atmosphere for their customers. They are efficiently organized

and stocked, offering a variety of merchandise to fulfill a woman's distinctive clothing needs. Whether you need executive suits and separates as a working woman, elegant designer apparel for special occasions, sportswear for leisure or play or classic traditional styling, you'll find them at The Buccaneer.

Buccaneer lines include Adagio, Alan Paine, Burberry, Byford, Designi, Geiger, Gordon, Izod, J.G. Hook, JH Collectibles, Jones of New York, Justin, Lanz, Merona, Nantucket, Paula Saker, Pendleton, Sawyer, Sero and Thomson. The Buccaneer also provides private label merchandise, and a full line of accessories including scarves and ties, belts and pins, and shoes featuring Bass, Cole-Haan, Sperry and Trafalgar.

In addition to the Buccaneer's personal charge, Mastercard, Visa and American Express are accepted.

Look forward to two new Buccaneer stores. The first, in Colorado Springs, opens in July 1982; the second, to open in Southwest Plaza, in March 1983.

Polo by Ralph Lauren

Downtown
410 17th Street
825-3884

Cherry Creek
231 Detroit Street
399-3277

University Hills Shopping Center
759-3558

Colorado Springs
204 N. Tejon
633-3889

Those who long for a "bygone" era when things were created not only to endure, but to improve with age, will be heartened to know that these qualities prevail at Perkins Shearer stores. Fashion, quality, value and cheerful expertise are alive and well, tempered by a hundred and ten years of experience and tradition in the Colorado marketplace.

When Perkins Shearer was founded in Colorado Springs in 1872, a gentleman required a wardrobe of sturdy stuff as he went about the business of taming the rugged frontier. Then, as now, men demanded more than simple protection from the elements. The priorities of such men gave rise to clothing designed to deal with requirements of taste and function combined.

Chamois by Ralph Lauren

Today, women as well as men look to Perkins Shearer as a reliable source of the finest quality clothing, accessories, shoes and gifts for all occasions. One visit makes this fact obvious. Perkins Shearer enjoys an exclusive association with the renowned American designer, Ralph Lauren, and features a Ralph Lauren Polo Shop within their Cherry Creek store. Also represented are designers Alexander Julian, Peter Barton, Jhane Barnes, Norma Kamali, Calvin Klein, Terry Ellis and a diverse selection of Perkins Shearer private label fashions to complement the superb quality and fascinating variety available.

Further, the hand-picked staff of thoroughly knowledgeable sales people capably provides customers with genuine assistance and professional advice.

Perkins Shearer
est. 1872

NEUSTETERS

Downtown
720 16th Street
534-3311

Cherry Creek
1st Ave. at Milwaukee
321-0880

Southglenn Mall
University at Arapahoe Road
795-3060

Boulder
2410 Arapahoe
442-9130

Is there such a thing as "the Denver woman"? You bet. She's much like the city and the region she lives in: free spirited, bold, independent, full of visions of limitless horizons.

And the Denver woman is not something new on the scene. We at Neusteters have been catering to this dynamic person for 70 years.

We've offered what she's demanded: the finest, most prestigious designer and couture lines, from classic, traditional styling to the latest in fashions. We've given her new ideas in gifts and accessories for the men and children in her life.

For her we created our beautiful Empire Salon, which carries our most exclusive items: captivating sportswear, dresses, evening wear designed by such couturiers as Bill Blass, Geoffrey Beene, Mary McFadden, Oscar de la Renta, Valentino. Tailored to the individual, couture fashion is unbelievably complimentary to today's woman. The Empire Salon also carries complete, one-of-a-kind accessories.

For the active, professional career woman there's our Neusportif department, offering sensible working fashions, including separates. Nuance is for the young junior, with a contemporary overtone. All our fashions are seasonally coordinated.

We feature departments for lingerie, millinery, hosiery, gloves and handbags. Our jewelry department carries fresh, exciting designs from contemporary to antique Chinese pieces. Our full-service fur salon includes storage, repair, and restyling. A complete international fragrance boutique can be found in our cosmetic department.

Exclusive to Denver is our Jaeger Shop, located in our downtown store, bringing that well-coordinated collection of British wools and seasonal ensembles. Downtown and at our Cherry Creek store, Mr. Mack Hair Design Centers serve the Denver woman with hairstyling that meets her needs, from conservative to avant garde.

For convenience we offer three locations in Denver and one in Boulder, including our main store downtown in the heart of the new 16th Street mall.

Jewelry by Tapestry/Cherry Creek

Michael
OF THE CARLYLE INC.

755 S. Colorado Blvd.
777-7722

Staying abreast of the times is a long tradition at Michael of the Carlyle and Peter's Place. When Mr. Michael Damien opened his salon at the Carlyle Hotel in New York City in 1938, his shop quickly became a trendsetter. He moved the company to Denver in 1955 and maintained the practice of offering the most advanced styling to his clients.

Today, Michael's is owned by three Europeans, Stefan Horvath from Austria, Fred Sauer from Germany and Peter Berger from Switzerland. All three are accomplished European hair designers in their own right.

Michael of the Carlyle and Peter's Place serves its large clientele with the latest, most efficient technology. This is the only beauty salon in the area with all 18 locations on a central computer system. The computer handles every appointment like an airline reservation system, giving better service and more efficient scheduling.

But computerization is only one way that Michael of the Carlyle is keeping in step with modern trends. Every year, the company's hairdressers are required to attend classes to update their knowledge and techniques. The style directors on the staff frequently attend seminars and fashion shows in the United States and Europe so they can bring the latest styles and methods to Denver.

In addition to hair design services, Michael's offers facials, manicures, pedicures, makeup application and lessons in the latest personal care techniques. A few of the salons also carry boutique clothing for a discriminating clientele. The broad range of hair styling services available is most impressive—from simple cuts and sets to advanced frosting and highlighting techniques for hair of any length. Problem hair and very long hair pose no problem for Michael of the Carlyle's trained designers.

The decor, also, reflects the lifestyle of Michael's clients. Each salon is customized to appeal to the area it services. The total experience of their customers is the primary concern at Michael of the Carlyle and Peter's Place. For personal care you can trust, call our central reservation number at 777-7722.

1037 Broadway
534-7400

JONAS BROS., INC.

Denver's most prominent citizens as well as celebrities of the world have crossed the portals of Jonas Bros., Inc. in Denver. Once inside, one can expect the highest quality and experience necessary to assure complete service for the purchase and maintenance of your fur.

Jonas Bros.' special knowledge of fur stems from their long and extensive work in taxidermy, in which they have earned a worldwide reputation. This special knowledge allows them to provide service and quality rarely found under one roof.

They can design and manufacture fur garments for clients who bring in their own skins, such as: coyote, beaver, and fox. If you own an heirloom fur, in most instances they can alter, repair, or restyle it right on the premises. There is no jobbing out your garment to a furrier who doesn't work directly with you.

Jonas Bros., Inc. also works closely with New York designers in providing custom furs for the individual who needs special attention in fitting or prefers a change in the color or fashion of the fur she selects from Jonas Bros.' elegant showroom.

A cold storage vault and complete cleaning facilities also are located at Jonas Bros. to insure proper care of your furs.

Jonas Bros. has a wide selection of furs, from casual and sport furs to the most elegant, in traditional to contemporary styles. Designer furs include fashions by Stephen Burrows and Geoffrey Beene, and labels such as: Royal Crown Sable, Blackglama Mink, EMBA Mink, Saga Fox, and Swakara Lamb.

The staff is always eager to serve you. And, they are particularly experienced and knowledgeable because Jonas Bros., Inc. has specialized in furs since they first opened their store in 1908.

Mr. Coloman Jonas, the founder of Jonas Bros., Inc., is known as the "Father of Modern Taxidermy" having pioneered and set the standards in sculpting and mounting animal trophies. Today Jonas Bros. is the world's largest and foremost manufacturer of many of the items used in taxidermy. They have won countless awards in national taxidermy competitions. Whether mounting your desert bighorn, bringing to life a prize-winning fish, or making a long-lasting bear rug, Jonas Bros. is the undisputed master.

Pollyanna

Lingerie & Accessories

**Tamarac Square
7777 E. Hampden Ave.
755-5032**

**Hours: Mon.-Fri. 10 am-9 pm
Sat. 10-6, Sun. 12-5**

For the woman who cares about herself and the man who cares about his lady, Pollyanna is a paradise. To look and touch and dream a little in this small, casually elegant, Victorian style shop in Tamarac Square is, as they say, "a little slice of heaven."

Pollyanna is the place to buy little silky wisps of matching bras and panties, long, stunningly elegant satin robes, pert teddies and camisole tops, soft white cotton nightgowns trimmed in Victorian lace, fanciful tap pants, boudoir accessories and so much more! From basic to breathtaking—Pollyanna has it—or will get it for you.

Pollyanna has grown in five years from a 350-square-foot "shopette"—to a 1200 square-foot boutique with an appropriately burgeoning stock. The reason, of course, is Beverly Day, a bright, engaging woman who says, "I've been in the lingerie business for six years, and in retailing forever!" She was anxious to bring in designers and styles available nowhere else in Colorado.

Pollyanna's patrons become almost addicted to the beauty and versatility they find in undergarments and sleepwear of every type and style, and the personal service that guarantees them a custom fit each time they make a purchase. Petite and other hard-to-fit sizes are not a problem at Pollyanna. Hems are raised or lowered, straps taken up, tucks put here and there—whatever is needed to enhance the appeal of the garment is done at no charge, certainly an unusual service in the lingerie business.

There is no "typical customer" at Pollyanna. From a dreamy-eyed bride searching for that perfect peignoir to a grandmother delighting in a return to classical elegance in sleepwear, all find what they're looking for, and then some.

Beverly and her staff become personally involved with Pollyanna clients, so it's no surprise that most of her business is repeat and referral. Always innovative, she has begun a bridal registry. Most of her clients already have a size and preference chart on file.

Since men feel comfortable browsing in the shop as well, Beverly is introducing a line of silk kimonos, pajamas and boxer shorts for them.

Denver Jean Co.

Tamarac Square
3333 So. Tamarac Dr.
750-8842

Mon. - Fri. 10-9
Saturday 10-6; Sunday 12-5

You might find Brooke Shields or O.J. Simpson browsing through the merchandise at Denver Jean Company, if they lived in Denver. This is the store that stocks the Calvin Kleins and fashion boots they prefer.

Denver Jean Company in Tamarac Square puts its emphasis on fashion and designer styles in men's and women's casual wear. Opened in August of 1980 by Rick Lebovitz, Denver Jean Company is for those who demand quality in goods and services.

As the name implies, a large and varied stock of jeans is available— Levi's, Lee's, Jordache, Generra, Brittania, Gloria Vanderbilt, JouJou, Manisha, and many more fine designer fashions. But it doesn't stop there. At Denver Jean Company, designer labels are not enough and Rick takes great care in helping his clients find what suits them best, whether they be teenagers or grandmothers.

There is no need to risk taking that new pair of Cacharel jeans home and finding that they aren't quite right. If fitting you properly requires alterations, that service is performed at no charge. "Everyone wants to look good," Rick says. "I think our customers have found that we have the fashions they want, but most importantly, that we have the knowledge to give them the very best fit possible."

In addition to jeans, Denver Jean Company has a wide selection of unusual sweaters, tops, accessories and top quality boots to complement your wardrobe.

So even if you don't encounter a celebrity at Denver Jean Company, at least you can shop with the confidence that you'll come out with clothes as good looking and well fitting as theirs.

CJI

W. Russell Ohlson

2865 South Colorado Blvd.
753-1110

The old saying that one picture is worth
a thousand words certainly does apply
to the scenic and portrait photography
of W. Russell Ohlson. With more than
twenty years' professional experience,
Ohlson's photographs transcend all
verbal descriptions.

Wherever Russell Ohlson sets up his camera—in one of his three Denver area studios or anywhere outdoors—he blends
all his craftsmanship with an eye for detail and an instinct for that perfect moment. His personal style is expressed in
unique composition, through sensitivity to
the interplay between light and shadow.

Photography

This dedication to excellence has won him national acclaim. His scenic photography and portraits can be found in galleries, public buildings, private clubs and distinguished homes throughout the Rocky Mountain region. Ohlson was the personal family photographer for Governors John Love, John Vanderhoof, and Richard Lamm; and provided President and Mrs. Reagan with photographic coverage of their 1980 campaign trips to Colorado.

Portraits are his specialty, particularly in natural and outdoor environments. But Ohlson also is a distinguished fine art photographer in exquisite Rocky Mountain settings. In addition to many local, regional and national awards, he is one of a few photographers in the area to meet all the requirements for the coveted Master of Photography degree from the Professional Photographers Association of America.

Versatility is his trademark. He has handled portraiture for weddings, families (together and separately), graduates, business executives and special events. He is also owner of the Reflections Gallery at The Lodge in Vail. In addition to Ohlson's scenic photography, the gallery carries the finest contemporary polished bronze sculptures in the region.

Photography is more than just a profession for W. Russell Ohlson; it's a way of life.

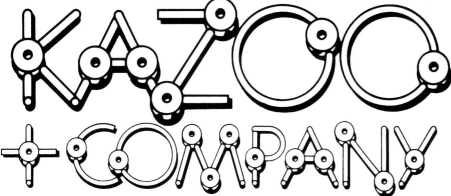

2364 E. 3rd Ave.
322-0973

An enchanting menagerie of toys is living at Kazoo & Company. Toys that stimulate discovery, creativity, and growth. Toys that can make your child's world a magical, joyful place.

Owner Beth Griffiths has carefully selected each toy with children in mind, from infants through young adults. Great care has been taken to offer toys which invite a child to be an active participant, to create, to imagine, to pretend, to learn.

Toys range from the unusual and intriguing to such classics as hardwood unit blocks, probably still the number one toy for children. And no child—or adult—can resist Kazoo's collection of dolls, one of the largest selections in town.

Kazoo is one of the largest toy stores in Denver, with two full floors offering such lines as Lego, Fisher - Price, Effanbee dolls and Estes rockets as well as many imported toys including Steiff plush animals, German dolls, and Ambi, Brio and Simper infant toys.

The Kazoo staff, knowledgeable in

child development, is always ready to help you select the proper toy for your child. The store's spacious, inviting, clearly grouped displays make selection easier too.

Two of the most popular sections are the art supplies department with a wide assortment of paper and art materials and the science section offering micro-scopes, magnifiers, science kits and more to encourage children to explore their world.

The store has an exceptional book section, as well as a section any parent can appreciate—toys especially de-signed to be played with while traveling.

Naturally children are welcomed and enjoyed at Kazoo. Special play areas for them include an art table, block play area, and a reading corner complete with a truck cab to climb into.

Kazoo will gift wrap anything you purchase free of charge, and children can make a card to go with a present for a friend.

So if you have children, are planning them, or are a child at heart, drop in to Kazoo & Company. Your child will be fascinated—and so will you.

Jewelry

The Rocky Mountain Empire was built on gold and silver. The beauty and inherent value of those precious metals, enhanced by today's expert craftsmanship, are offered, along with rare gems and minerals, at these fine jewelry stores and gift shops.

Pull a penny out of your pocket and examine it. Is there a tiny D stamped just below the printing date? If so, it was produced at the U.S. Mint in Denver, which stamps out more than 6 billion coins a year, from pennies to quarters. ⤢ The Denver Mint opened for business as a U.S. assay office in 1863 in facilities acquired from a private mint. Although busy assaying the wealth of gold pouring out of the Rocky Mountains, the Mint did not begin actual coinage until 1906, after it moved to its present location at West Colfax and Delaware St. ⤢ Built from granite, its windows heavily-barred, the Mint is an impregnable-looking structure. It's meant to be. Besides being one of only two fully operational mints in the country, churning out $175,000 worth of coins daily, it is the second largest depository of gold, behind Ft. Knox. ⤢ The imposing Gothic Renaissance architecture has done its job deterring anyone pondering get-rich-quick schemes. There has never been an armed assault directly on the Mint, though a heavily-armed gang in the 1920s did relieve a Federal Reserve Bank truck of $200,000 in front of the Mint. Holes in the marble vestibule of the Mint chipped out by the exchange of gunfire are still visible. ⤢ An easier way to get into the Denver Mint is by taking a tour. It's a noisy, fun-filled tour, about 30 minutes long. You'll see the stamping operations as well as some of the building's fine interior architecture. If you appreciate gold, you'll especially want to see the display of six gold bars. Each bar weighs 27½ pounds and the display is worth around $1 million. Souvenir coin sets, national medals, and other numismatic items are on sale at the Mint. ⤢ Visitors flock to the Mint, especially in the summer, so be prepared to wait in line. Tours are 8:00 a.m. to 3:30 p.m. May 1 to October 1 and from 8:30 a.m. to 3:00 p.m. October 1 to May 1. The Mint is closed to visitors weekends, holidays, and for two weeks during each summer for inventory (inquire before visiting.)

Argenzio Brothers

8 locations:

Downtown
900 16th
629-6249

Northglenn Mall
104th Ave. and I-25
452-5678

Cinderella City
701 W. Hampden Ave.
781-6697

Southglenn Mall
6911 S. University
795-1221

Aurora Mall
Alameda Ave. and I-225
343-9822

Tiffany Plaza
7400 E. Hampden
770-9086

Boulder
Crossroads Mall
449-8014

Fort Collins
Foothills Fashion Mall
629-7769 (Denver no.)

The best surprise is the perfect gift at the perfect moment, and the best surprises begin at Argenzio Brothers.

Argenzio's expertise is in engagements, anniversaries, graduations or simply the spontaneous expression of love. Argenzio Brothers has been helping people surprise their loved ones with beautiful jewelry and unforgettable giftware for 57 years.

For that very special woman, consider a stunning ensemble necklace of emeralds, rubies, sapphires, and diamonds set in 14 karat gold.

Or try a Pave diamond bracelet to remind someone of your special love. Cultured pearl studs may ideally suit the woman in your life.

Whatever the occasion or the need, Argenzio Brothers offers one of the area's finest and widest selections. Rolex, Concord, Omega, and Seiko watches. Benchmark and Swiza clocks. A large selection of 14 karat gold, including chains, earrings, and bracelets. Waterford full lead crystal, blown and cut entirely in Ireland. Porcelain figurines by Lladro of Spain. Many other gift ideas including Lalique crystal, Fukagawa porcelain, Reed and Barton silver, and Baldwin candlesticks.

Everything is of uncommon excellence, and Argenzio Brothers' staff will insure that your visit to one of their elegantly designed stores is a memorable experience. In addition to their fine jewelry, Argenzio Brothers provides appraisals, jewelry and watch repair, and custom manufacturing.

Don't miss an opportunity to express to someone how much you really care. Surprise him or her with the perfect gift.

William Crow

Jewelers
since 1924

**910 16th Street
292-2350**

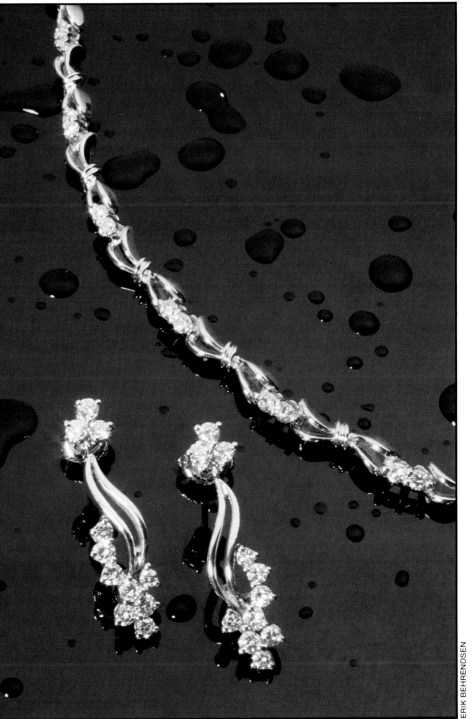

ERIK BEHRENDSEN

Unspoken elegance. Timelessness. Value. The essence of all fine jewelry is found at William Crow jewelers.

Quality. Experience. Professionalism. Jewelry as personal and sincere as the service is found at William Crow.

Since 1924, William Crow Jewelers has served Denver . . . in some cases as many as four generations. Being one of Denver's largest locally owned, independent jewelers, William Crow has never wavered in its commitment to quality, trust, and fair pricing.

Compare.

William Crow offers the finest in diamonds, precious stones (set and unset), gold chains, earrings, bracelets, gold watches by Concord, its own designer series of watches, a complete silver department and gift section.

Major jewelry lines include Oscar Heyman, Terrel & Co., Seiko, Harry Winston, and Gem Veto. Crow represents Towle, Reed & Barton, Gorham, and others in its fine silver department.

With skill and pride that is rarely found today, William Crow Jewelers can redesign and remodel your out-of-date or worn jewelry pieces, repair all jewelry and watches, engrave those memorable items, and provide expert appraisals — all in surroundings of friendly, comfortable, professional elegance.

The high quality jewelry, the expertise, the commitment to excellence speaks for itself: the vast majority of new customers at William Crow are referred by existing customers.

When it comes to trust, word of mouth is as precious as fine jewelry.

Take the elevator up to the third floor University Building downtown on the mall at 16th & Champa for quality and experience at fair prices. It's worth the trip.

EUGENE ROSE
Jeweler/Gemologist

**740 S. Colorado Blvd.
in the Galleria
759-3900**

At Eugene Rose, they believe that no jewelry store can be everything to everyone. So they don't try. But what they do, they do best: gemology, diamonds, natural colored gemstones, and karat gold jewelry.

As members of the American Gem Society, Eugene Rose offers an extensive collection of natural colored gemstones from around the world.

In addition to the more familiar Ruby, Emerald, and Sapphire, they can show you such rare stones as Andalusite, Kunzite, Alexandrite, Rhodochrosite, Rubellite, Tanzanite, Star Ruby, Padparadscha Sapphire, Lilac Topaz, Cat's Eye Tourmaline, Chrysoberyl Cat's Eye, or a strand of Opal Beads. If your stone is not mentioned, call and see if they have it. If they don't they will find one for you. Or they may have a natural diamond in your favorite color.

Eugene Rose carries both the traditional and the unusual in jewelry design. Their skilled, imaginative craftsmen create some of the most beautiful jewelry you'll find anywhere.

All this is housed in a beautifully designed, mellow setting. The display areas are set among natural plants and subdued lighting, with comfortable seating at the display cases.

The unusual round shape of the Appraisal Room lends an open, bright environment, with special lighting for viewing fine jewelry as well as doing laboratory work. The room won a national jeweler's award for Most Innovative Design.

But no firm is better than the people in it, and this is what Eugene Rose excels in. Begun by Eugene Rose more than a generation ago, the tradition of exceptional jewelry has been carried on by Yvonne Rose and a staff dedicated to doing what they do the very best.

HydePark

**Tamarac Square
7777 East Hampden
755-3541**

**Monday - Friday 10-9
Sat. 10-6; Sun. 12-5**

Just after entering Hyde Park in Tamarac Square, you begin to sense that this is not a run-of-the-mill jewelry store. Hyde Park has a special ambience—a casual but elegant atmosphere; a non-traditional air that exudes a classic style, a cleanness of form.

Hyde Park is a reflection of its owners, Michael Pollak and Steve Rosdall; their pride and care to present the best; their desire to have their clientele represent the epitome of look and design.

As with most jewelry stores, Hyde Park offers gold, precious and semi-precious stones, crystal, watches, stemware, lighters, pens, and a variety of accessories. But few other stores have their own custom designer in residence.

Phillip Stone, an award-winning designer, crafts many of the designs on display and will design that distinctive piece to fit your individual desire. In keeping with the commitment to excellence, all jewelry at Hyde Park is the work of designers throughout the world: New York, London, Paris, Milan and other centers of the jeweler's art.

The list of quality merchandise avail-able at Hyde Park is vast. Lighters and pens by S.T. DuPont, crafted with such attention to detail that they take longer to produce than a Mercedes-Benz. Stemware and crystal by Lalique, Daum, and Saint Louis of France. The famous watch collection by les Must de Cartier. Corum timepieces with movements integrated into rare gold coins. Movado, Seiko, Pulsar and Concord. That is just a small sample.

For the busy executive, Hyde Park also offers a Corporate Sales service. A sales representative will come to your office or place of business to help select that special gift or award.

Whether your purchase costs $50 or $15,000, Hyde Park is an establishment that assures you of buying the finest in goods and services. That, in the final analysis, is what value is all about.

FOSTER & SON

THE 14 KARAT

Cherry Creek North
233 Steele Street
377-1414

Hours: Mon.-Fri. 10 a.m.-5:30 p.m.
Sat. 10 a.m.-4 p.m.

Foster and Son is a family-owned business that has served Denver with a "special touch" for a quarter of a century.

Patty and Brien Foster sell the finest jewelry and gifts manufactured. They have customers who return again and again, confident that they will receive nothing less than the highest of quality served with that "special touch" of individual attention.

Every purchase is important at Foster and Son. The Fosters, the staff and the talented goldsmiths spend as much time as the customer needs to arrive at the best choice. Be it a Patek Phillippe watch, a silver bowl or amusing stocking present from the superb gift department, a special piece of jewelry designed just for you, or your antique piece to be redesigned or any kind of repair, Foster and Son thinks that you are special and will work closely with you.

Discover for yourself that Foster and Son is one of the most distinctive and complete stores in Denver. Ample stock displayed with careful elegance offers a wide choice in both variety and price. If you do not find exactly the right piece they will get it for you or make it.

Foster and Son is proud of its long established reputation. "Our special pride is the people we serve. The most satisfying part of our business is meeting old and new customers and building friendships as a result of mutual trust."

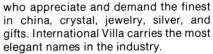

international villa

Cherry Creek North
262 Fillmore
333-1524

Marina Square
8101 E. Belleview
773-2130

To describe International Villa as just another bride and gift shop is to describe a Rolls-Royce as just another car.

This is a very special place for people who appreciate and demand the finest in china, crystal, jewelry, silver, and gifts. International Villa carries the most elegant names in the industry.

Whether it's Baccarat Crystal (the crystal of kings since 1764), limited edition Cybis porcelain sculptures, fine diamonds, Piaget watches, Wedgwood English china, Lalique crystal or high fashion jewelry, you know everything is international in scope and the best possible value for the price.

The diversity meets all budgets, and has earned International Villa a special place in the hearts of Denver area brides.

The store's policy has always been one of dedication to excellence and a long-standing commitment to providing the finest bridal registry service for Denver's oldest families and its most discriminating newcomers.

The Villa's bridal consultants are trained to give brides that special service and attention. The vast selection makes finding something perfect a certainty.

International Villa carries Lenox china, Waterford crystal, sterling silver by Buccellati, pearls, country French-styled earthenware by Longchamp, and Boehm's exquisite porcelain sculptures of birds and flowers.

You'll find these names—and much, much more—at International Villa. It's like strolling down Fifth Avenue.

Sports

**Do you love to fish? Watch pro football—
live? Play racquetball? Swim? Take a
seventh-inning stretch on a warm summer's night? Here are the finest in
athletic clubs, sports equipment stores,
and pro teams.**

Mile High Stadium is as close to a shrine as anything in Denver. Each fall it is the mecca toward which all eyes turn as the Denver Broncos play their tough National Football League schedule before 75,000 screaming, orange-clad fans. Broncomania, this gridiron madness is called, and if you're new to Denver you probably have never experienced anything quite like it before. ⅛ Denver is a sports-hungry town. The stadium, home to the Broncos and the Triple-A baseball club, the Denver Bears, has gone through several expansions to satisfy the hunger. Originally called Bears Stadium, the facility was constructed in 1948 for the baseball team. Seats were added in 1959 and 1968, after the Broncos were formed. In 1974, Denver voters approved a $25 million bond issue to improve and expand the stadium to its present 75,000-seat capacity. Not only is the stadium Denver's largest public facility, it also is its most remarkable with a unique 16,000-seat movable east stand that slides on a .003-inch curtain of water—fully extended for football, retracted for baseball. ⅛ Other spectator sports have fared well in Denver. Two parking lots away is McNichols Arena, home of the National Basketball Association's Denver Nuggets, the Colorado Rockies pro hockey team, and the new indoor soccer league team, the Denver Avalanche. Denver also hosts an annual Ladies Professional Golf Association tournament, the United Bank Tennis Classic which draws top seeds, and portions of the increasingly popular Coors Bicycle Classic. Professional horse and dog racing are popular. And there is always the fervent gossip about bringing a major league baseball team to Denver. ⅛ But Denver is more than a spectator town. Coloradans tend to be active, outdoor people. On a summer afternoon the tennis courts, golf courses, and softball diamonds are packed. Hiking, fishing, skiing, and even sailing attract Denver citizens. Athletic clubs abound, and joggers are everywhere, rain or shine, except of course on crisp fall Sunday afternoons, when the Broncos are in town and Mile High Stadium is a noisy, orange canyon of thrills.

DENVER BRONCOS

Ticket office: Denver Mile High Stadium
1900 Eliot St.
433-7466

Any story about the Denver Broncos is certainly as much a story of its fans as it is of its team, players, and coaches. Few teams in all professional sports have enjoyed such intense and loyal support from its fans as have the Broncos.

Even before the "miracle" of 1977, when the Broncos won their first American Football Conference championship and went to the Super Bowl, Bronco fans were demonstrating their enthusiasm. Every regular season game since 1969 has been sold out, and the waiting list today for season tickets has climbed above 11,000.

Why such dedicated support? Win or lose, the Denver Broncos have always produced exciting teams and exciting

players. The Broncos were organized in 1959, a charter member of the American Football League. They played and won their first AFL game, against the Boston Patriots on Sept. 9, 1960.

The fans then turned out to see such Bronco all pros as Goose Gonsoulin, Bud McFadin, and the great Lionel Taylor, who won four straight pass receiving titles and was the first AFL player to catch 500 passes.

During those early years in the AFL, the Broncos quickly emerged as one of the leaders in home attendance. When the AFL merged with the National Football League in 1966 attendance and season ticket sales surged dramatically, and by 1968 attendance was averaging an impressive 33,000 a game.

The 1970s brought such greats as Otis Armstrong, Rick Upchurch, and Craig Morton. Players like Lyle Alzado, Randy Gradishar, and Tom Jackson

helped make Denver's feared defense one of the finest ever to play pro football. And, of course, 1977 will forever be etched in the hearts of Bronco fans, as Denver's "Cinderella" team had its finest season ever, going 12-2 and playing Dallas in the Super Bowl. In an effort to keep pace with the growing enthusiasm of the fans, Mile High Stadium, the Broncos' largest home, was enlarged in 1977 to 75,103 seats, becoming the seventh largest home facility in the NFL.

The 1980s sees the Broncos under the new ownership of industrialist Edgar F. Kaiser, Jr. New General Manager Grady Alderman and Head Coach Dan Reeves continued the Broncos' great tradition of exciting football, finishing the 1982 season with an impressive 10-6 record. Two decades of great football, and for the ever-loyal Bronco fans, the 1980s promise to be the best years ever.

DenverNuggets

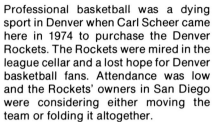

Professional basketball was a dying sport in Denver when Carl Scheer came here in 1974 to purchase the Denver Rockets. The Rockets were mired in the league cellar and a lost hope for Denver basketball fans. Attendance was low and the Rockets' owners in San Diego were considering either moving the team or folding it altogether.

But Scheer had faith in Denver's basketball fans. Forming a coalition of 30 local businessmen, the former assistant commissioner of the National Basketball Association bought the Rockets and promised the team would always be Denver-owned and Denver-operated. All the faith and all the promises meant nothing, though, unless Scheer could pull the team out of its losing ways.

The first order of business was changing the team's public image. The Denver Rockets became the Denver Nuggets. New team colors were chosen. A new team logo was designed. A new head coach, Larry Brown, was brought in, and new players were acquired. The total package worked.

In their first season, the Denver Nuggets set several ABA records and won the division championship. Scheer proclaimed that Denver now had a "winning tradition" and the fans believed him. The Nuggets have since had good years and bad, but Denver basketball fans have always supported their team.

Last year's Nuggets team broke a two year slump by setting nine NBA records during the regular season. The 1982 Nuggets were the all-time high-scoring team in NBA history, averaging 126.5 points per game, the first team in the 36-year-old NBA to score more than 100 points every game. Coming on with a rush near season's end, the Nuggets entered the playoffs in the number four slot, vanquishing Phoenix in their opening playoff game and losing the best-of-three series in a heart-breaking finale.

Scheer and the fans keep the faith, and the Nuggets always come back from adversity. Scheer's goal is to keep the club intact. Under new head coach Doug Moe, the Nuggets will continue to play a fast running game. Pushing the offense for points will strengthen the defensive game. Win or lose in '83, the fans are guaranteed an exciting season.

For ticket information, write:
8000 E. Prentice Street
Building D, Suite 7
Denver Technological Center
Englewood, CO 80111

Indoor soccer adds an exciting new dimension to what has long been the most popular sport in the world. But indoors it's quicker, with more shots, more points, and suspenseful shoot-outs to decide game-ending ties.

The Denver Avalanche is right in the thick of it with an exciting, contending team in the Major Indoor Soccer League.

Denver fans have taken to the Avalanche, coming to games in great numbers. This fan support is phenomenal for a team that has existed only since 1980. The fans love the unequalled excitement of the game and the talented, go-for-broke, young American players.

They come too because, compared with other professional sports, indoor soccer is a superior entertainment buy. The inexpensive admission prices are coupled with an innovative season ticket selection. You can purchase a regular season ticket to all 22 home games, or you can buy season tickets for 6 or 11 games and pick the games you want to come to. A great deal for the busy family.

American players form the nucleus of the Avalanche, and the staff and coaches are steeped in soccer. For instance, club president Ron Maierhofer was an All-American striker at Cornell University and a member of the 1960 U.S. Olympic squad. Head Coach David Clements has achieved international renown as a member of the Northern Ireland National School Team and the New York Cosmos. He is the youngest man ever to coach a national team.

Join the indoor soccer fans at McNichols. Listen to the Avalanche roar.

BRUCE HARPER

![Colorado Rockies logo]

COLORADO ROCKIES

General office
573-1800

Ticket office
534-7825

The fans jump to their feet as the announcer's voice booms from the McNichols Arena loudspeakers, "Here come the Rockies!" Applause becomes a roar when Denver's professional hockey team enters the rink, sharp blades flashing on the new ice. The players circle the rink, passing several pucks between them, practicing slapshots as the goaltender takes his position. The referees give a signal and all but the two starting teams clear the ice. The opening face-off is tense, restless. At last the referee slams down the puck between the two opposing centers. The game is on!

This is Rocky Hockey, a fast-paced physical game filled with break away excitement and teamwork precision. Spectacular saves by the goalie can send the crowd to its feet. A deft backhand shot into the net can have the fans crying for more. And when a player is checked hard against the boards, everyone moans and waits anxiously to see who ends up with the puck.

The Colorado Rockies came to Denver in 1976 when oilman Jack Vickers purchased the bankrupt Kansas City Scouts. With hard work, the Rockies made it to the playoffs in 1978. Vickers sold the team, before the next season began, to trucking magnate Arthur Imperatore who in turn sold the team mid-season in 1981 to cable-TV wizard Peter Gilbert.

Gilbert was determined to revitalize the team and see Denver winning once again. He spent more money on new players and staff than all the previous owners combined. The 1981-82 season started slowly but picked up momentum. The fans supported this effort and were rewarded with thrill-packed action.

Denver is a hockey town. When the public rinks open in late fall, hundreds of kids don helmets and shin pads, dreaming of being a pro, winning that one-on-one confrontation with the goalie. These same kids go to the Rockies' games, hoping to catch a loose puck flipped out of the rink. Their folks join in the fun, urging the Rockies to victory.

Last year's Rocky Hockey team laid the foundation for success this coming season. Like a Bobby Orr slapshot, the Colorado Rockies will remain unforgettable.

the denver bears

There are some words that shouldn't be used lightly in sports. But here is the one word that can properly describe the Denver Bears baseball team:

Dynasty.

In the past dozen-odd years, the Bears, or Grizzlies as they're sometimes called, have won seven Western Divisional titles and four American Association league championships.

The 1980 team amassed an incredible 92-44 regular season record and sent such players as the fleet-footed Tim Raines to the majors. That Grizzly juggernaut was called the nation's best Triple-A club in 20 years, and a major league scout said they were better than at least four of the major league teams.

The 1981 team, with a tough act to follow, did it in fine fashion by winning the league championship in four straight games over Omaha.

Bears' fans are something of a dynasty in their own right. The always-popular Fireworks Night in July drew 59,691 in 1981, breaking their own minor league attendance record set the year before. The Bears also hold the American Association's season attendance record with 565,214, set in 1980, a record the Bears nearly broke the following year.

The Bears expect to continue their dynasty throughout the '80s. And the Bears return to the fold of the Texas Rangers after six years under the Montreal Expos. They're sporting new uniforms, a new logo, and one thing from the old days. A tradition of winning.

Colorado Golf

When people think of Colorado history, they tend to recall gold and silver mines, the Unsinkable Molly Brown, Bonfils and Tammen, or Horace Tabor. But the game of golf is also a vital part of Colorado tradition.

The first golf course west of the Mississippi River, Patty Jewett, was built in 1898 in Colorado. A few years later, the Broadmoor resort was established with its expansive greens and fairways. For many decades, the Broadmoor set the pace for amateur golf in the United States, acting as the springboard for many golfers who later made it big in the pro circuit. Skiing may be the state's most popular winter sport, but golf holds sway (or is that swing?) when spring sets in. Denver's many fine country clubs are nationally known for their golf courses—Cherry Hills, Green Gables and Pinehurst being only a sampling. In addition, Denver features many quality municipal courses where the going gets rough even for the best players.

The same factors that attract thousands to Colorado's scenic mountains in the winter draw thousands to the high country in the summer for a splendid round of golf. Many of the famous skiing resorts, such as Vail, Beaver Creek and Keystone, are developing reputations for golf as well. With the help of such avid amateur and professional golfers as former President Jerry Ford, Jack Nicklaus, Robert Trent Jones and Jack Vickers, Colorado's mountain courses are increasingly popular.

New golf courses at the top ski resorts are now being built in the Colorado Rockies. Millions of dollars are being spent to create courses to challenge the most experienced professionals. Nicklaus has helped create Single Tree in Beaver Creek, Jones helped plan the course at Keystone, and Jerry Ford has brought together the nation's best golfers for his annual tournament in Vail.

The Professional Golf Association also likes Colorado. The three courses in Vail are being looked at by the PGA for inclusion in its pro tour. The PGA is also considering Castle Pines, the dream course created by Jack Vickers, as another stop. All of the major 1982 Women's PGA tournaments will be held in Colorado, and the 1985 PGA championship tournament will be held at Cherry Hills Country Club.

Golf in Colorado is an exceptional experience. The game is a tradition in the state that cannot help becoming more important in the coming years.

Celebrity

SPORTS CENTER

888 S. Colorado Blvd.
757-3321

Hours: Sun.-Thurs. 8:30 a.m.-2:00 a.m.
Fri.-Sat. 8:30 a.m.-4:00 a.m.

At a time when the demands of society constantly tug the family apart in all directions, it's reas-suring to know someone still cares about keeping the family together.

At Celebrity Sports Center we believe in family recreation . . . and we've got it all under one roof, the largest and finest family-oriented recreation complex in the country.

We specialize in families at Celebrity. Our roots go back to Walt Disney and Art Linkletter, two believers in strong family ties. Seeing a need for a new dimension in family recreation, they and other Hollywood celebrities opened Celebrity Lanes in 1960. Two years later Walt Disney Productions purchased Celebrity, renaming it Celebrity Sports Center. In 1979, a group of Denver businessmen purchased the Center and launched an extensive $3 million renovation and remodeling program.

Where else can your family find, year-round, and in one place:

• Eighty lanes of bowling, making it one of the largest bowling centers in the United States. They provide league bowling from Juniors to Prime-Time Seniors, with qualified instructors and a well-equipped Pro Shop available to help you. Celebrity is host to many City, State, and National tournaments including both Ladies' and Men's Professional Bowling Association.

• An Olympic-size swimming pool featuring the only all-weather, outdoor-indoor waterslides in the country. Two slides, 450 ft. long, starting the most thrilling 30 seconds of your life from a 60 ft. tower, winding through a tunnel, under a waterfall and splashing into the largest indoor swimming pool in the West. A third slide, for the young and young-at-heart, runs 175 ft. under a bridge and waterfall before spilling into the pool. Swim lessons are available for all levels and ages, starting with babies at 3 months old.

• A Family Fun Center, where your family can play the ever popular Skee Ball, go wild on Krazy Kars, and take aim at 40 different targets in the Shooting Gallery. In the three Game Arcades you can challenge 300 of the latest pinball, electronic and video games, or play pocket billiards in the same place where such greats as Minnesota Fats and Willie Mosconi have played.

• Three restaurants and free baby-sitting. Whether you want a fast meal, a relaxing dinner, or your favorite drink, try these restaurants. A supervised playroom is for children through six, allowing you and the rest of your family to enjoy all of Celebrity's many activities.

COLORADO ATHLETIC CLUB

Club Central
281 Broadway
778-6373

Club North
4890 Carr
420-4555

The Colorado Athletic Club has the dual distinction of being the state's largest athletic club and its center for racquetball action.

The Colorado Athletic Club has two locations, one downtown and one in Arvada. Both are designed to provide athletic excellence for the individual with the finest equipment, instruction, and programs.

All-purpose gymnasiums are used for year-round fitness classes, jogging, basketball, and volleyball. The latest in Nautilus equipment offers members, under supervision of trained instructors, total conditioning and strength training. Olympic and Universal weight equipment complement the conditioning.

The Colorado Athletic Club North, with its country club atmosphere, also features a complete health club with walk-in whirlpool, steam, and sauna. The Club's eight acres of athletic facilities, which make it one of the largest athletic clubs in the country, include an outdoor swimming pool, tennis courts, jogging track, and Denver's only out-

door handball courts.

But more than anything the Colorado Athletic Club is synonymous with racquetball. Club Central, the birthplace of racquetball in Denver, has 17 air conditioned courts, Club North 19. Excellent instruction programs, clinics, and exhibitions stimulate interest in action-packed tournaments, ladder, and league play.

The Athletic Club hosts the largest racquetball tournament in the Rocky Mountain Region, the Pepsi-Wilson Tournament, which brings 500 players. The state handball tournament is also hosted by the Athletic Club.

The Colorado Athletic Club—an athletic tradition second to none.

DAVE COOK

**14 convenient locations
For the store nearest you, call
892-1929**

Perhaps the philosophy of Dave Cook Sporting Goods Co. was best summed up by a nationally known columnist more than 40 years ago: "You've played square with that great body of people who had been waiting for some guy like yourself to come along," he wrote, "someone who would put the outdoors within reach of the ordinary fellow's pocketbook."

That policy of honest value, coupled with a wide selection as the West's largest sporting goods chain, still stands.

Everything imaginable for the outdoorsman and sports enthusiast can be found at Dave Cook. There are sporting guns and ammunition, archery and camping equipment, fishing tackle and reel repair, jogging suits, tennis rackets, cameras, snow and water skis, golf clubs and accessories.

In a continuing effort to provide the best at the lowest in price, Dave Cook over the years has introduced its own products. Streamwing Fishing Flies, Challenger Fishing Rods, Skitique Skiwear, and Golden Bear Sleeping Bags are a few examples of low overhead, low cost items.

Dave Cook offers one of the largest selections of sports shoes in the West. The annual ski sale and ABC (Angling, Backpacking, and Camping) Sale are as much a part of the Colorado sports scene as the Rocky Mountains.

Since 1925, area sportsmen have come to regard Dave Cook as an experienced and knowledgeable friend. The company is synonymous with the growth of sports and outdoor activities in the Rocky Mountains.

Since the 1930s it has sponsored, along with the Denver Post, the popular Big Trout Fishing Contest. It sponsors ski trips, clinics on golf and hunter safety. It supplies sports equipment to most of the amateur, school, and professional teams in the area.

But more than anything, Dave Cook has brought the great outdoors within reach of the ordinary guy. With 14 stores located along the Front Range, Dave Cook truly has become "The Gateway to the World of Sports."

THE SPORTING CLUB

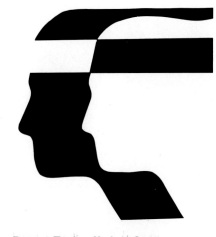

Denver Technological Center
5151 DTC Parkway
Englewood
779-0700

Cherry Creek
500 S. Cherry St.
Glendale
399-3050

Is your image of an athletic club someplace where sweaty fitness instructors crack whips and your racquetball partner plays as if he's going for the Olympic Gold? A place where it's a matter of shape up or ship out?

At The Sporting Club they believe that developing your physical abilities and becoming fit is important to your health and peace of mind, but that it is fun as well. To help you they have every imaginable kind of exercise and recreational facility at their two clubs in Cherry Creek and the Denver Tech Center.

If you love racquetball, or want to learn, they have plenty of courts with a full range of private and group lessons, leagues and clinics, challenge ladders, a special "Find-A-Partner" service, and tournaments.

If you want to shape up your body without putting it through some medieval torture chamber, The Sporting Club offers a variety of programs. Aerobics and dance exercise are very popular and fun. A special body-toning class is available for women. Have you ever considered the benefits of yoga? Not only an excellent conditioning program in itself, it enhances the other conditioning courses and reduces that modern-day killer—stress.

Aquanastics, or exercising in water, is a vigorous way to work out without the pain of sore muscles later. Or you can swim laps or take swimming instruction at the pool.

Nautilus equipment, perhaps the most efficient and scientific way to exercise, is available along with expert instruction on the equipment's use.

If you prefer the more challenging pursuits, The Sporting Club has established a mileage incentive program for biking, swimming, and running.

For relaxing afterwards, there are hot tubs, saunas, steam baths, Jacuzzis, and massage rooms, as well as a restaurant and bar at each club. For convenience, there is a pro shop and nursery. And to broaden your sense about your own body the club periodically schedules physicians, nutritionists, sports podiatrists, weight counselors, and other specialists.

AURORA ATHLETIC CLUB

2953 S. Peoria
750-3210

Good health and fitness is a fifty-fifty proposition. Half mental outlook, half exercise and diet. Perhaps that's why the Aurora Athletic Club has such dedicated, loyal members.

The club is much more than a fine array of facilities, equipment, and programs. It provides that special personal touch, that sense of family. It emphasizes friendliness and cleanliness. It's a place its members call "our club."

Such loyalty to a full-facility athletic club is due in part to the club's open-door policy. Says co-owner Orman Balzer, "People walk in our office, give us their thoughts, and we move the club accordingly. We have a genuine gratitude toward our members. They come to us and stay with us."

Of course, the heart of the club is its excellent facilities. With 12 racquetball courts, the club hosts leagues, ladders, challenges and tournaments. Professional instruction and an indoor run-ning track are added features. Its staff leads classes on aerobic conditioning, body toning, ski fitness, yoga, and pre-natal exercises.

In addition to the exercise programs, athletic director Bronko Lemke and assistant athletic director Cynthia Howard involve members in outside recreational leagues, parties, dances, BBQs, CPR classes, guest lectures on nutrition and health, sports clinics, and a host of other activities.

Conveniently located at I-225 and Parker Road, the Aurora Athletic Club provides a 7-day nursery, a well-equipped pro shop, saunas, steams, whirlpools, a bar and restaurant, and a cozy decor that enhances the home-like environment of this unusual athletic facility.

Uniquities

One of the joys of living in or visiting a large city like Denver is discovering those wonderfully unique or off-beat shops and services that make life a little bit richer. We've done some digging of our own and have compiled a list of treasures we think you shouldn't overlook.

Denver, though founded on gold, has always been very much a cowtown. Many prospectors brought cattle with them, and cattle were seen roaming the same Curtis Street that now grows steel and concrete. A few of the smarter prospectors, like John Wesley Iliff, became cattle barons feeding the hopeful and hungry. By the 1880s, Denver, as trail's end for many cattle drives, had become a major livestock center. ⚲ Cows don't roam Curtis Street these days. But part of Denver remains a cowtown, sometimes to the frustration of its more cosmopolitan souls. At no time does this cowtown heritage surface more vigorously than for ten days each January when the National Western Stock Show throws open its corrals and arenas. ⚲ It's the biggest event of the year for the Queen City of the Plains. ⚲ The National Western began in 1906 in a huge canvas tent with 351 cattle entries. It was an immediate success and within 20 years it eclipsed all other stock shows. Today, several huge buildings and dozens of livestock pens sprawl over 100 acres at I-70 and Lafayette. Attendance nudges 400,000 and 15,000 head of livestock are on hand. ⚲ For entertainment there are 21 rodeo performances—the second richest rodeo purse on the professional circuit. There is also the selection of the Grand Champion steer, a sheep shearing contest, draft horse pull, 4-H exhibits, and hundreds of commercial and educational exhibits. For ranchers and farmers livestock sales exceed $10 million. For Denver's economy, the Stock Show brings more than $35 million in retail sales. ⚲ For those cosmopolitan souls, the National Western is that time when even they can boldly dust off their hidden Stetsons and cowboy boots and join a part of the West that has never died.

EPICUREAN CATERING.

469 S. Cherry
321-0343

When you're drawing up that special guest list for your next soiree, don't forget to add the name Epicurean Catering. They'll be the life of the party.

Whether for a formal dinner at eight, a *fête champêtre*, or a special occasion, Epicurean Catering specializes in creative, custom designed catering that will add that special something to your entertainment.

There's no take-it-or-leave-it menu, no preconceived, prepackaged party plans at Epicurean. Let your imagination go. Want to host an "Old West" party complete with gunslingers serving two-inch thick T-bones from the back of a chuckwagon? Or a "Speakeasy" party with a gangster at the front door and hooch served in teacups? The professionals at Epicurean will attend to every detail, from renting the props to preparing and serving the cuisine.

The food is always of the finest, freshest quality, from tantalizing hors d'oeuvres to flaky French pastries, carefully prepared by Epicurean's chefs. And Epicurean's experienced hosts and hostesses are dedicated to making your guests—and you—have the time of your lives.

Invite Epicurean to your next affair. They'll turn a mere party into a memorable event.

THE FRUIT BASKET
and FRUIT COUNTRY STORES

1310 E. 6th Ave.
744-9079

3487 S. Logan
789-3401

5911 S. University Blvd.
794-0122

For more than 30 years the Fruit Basket and Fruit Country Stores have been offering to the discriminating cooks in the Denver area a truly exciting commodity: excellence in food and service.

They maintain one of the most complete selections of fresh fruits and vegetables to be found anywhere. From oranges and apples to fresh herbs and salad items, the quality is exceptional.

Just think about it . . . strawberries . . . gooseberries and blueberries in December . . . mangoes and papayas the year 'round!

But the Fruit Basket and Fruit Country Stores don't stop there . . . features include the S&W canned goods line, and the finest in vinegars, dressings and condiments. The cheese department offers over 150 varieties of imported and domestic cheeses. And the spotlight is on superb triple creams and cheesecakes!

Whole bean coffees are roasted and blended in-house and the array of teas and spices will certainly please any connoisseur.

Let's go one step further and find fresh baked goods, Devon cream in the dairy case, gourmet ice creams, Beluga caviar and fresh frozen truffles. . . .

You must consider the Fruit Basket and Fruit Country Stores the food emporium of the Rocky Mountains!

Silver Medal Award — 1982 National Pool and Spa Institute

10815 W. Jewell
989-6750

Picking a pool or spa is a decision you'll live with for a long time. That's why more and more people are coming to San Juan Pools and Spas. Who else gives you not only a great-looking pool but a 25-year warranty?

San Juan Pools and Spas come in 20 models, in a variety of shapes, sizes, and colors. Ranging from the compact Port-a-Spa to the 45-foot "Superstars," the models can match any outdoor or indoor setting you may have.

The pools and spas are one-piece fiberglass units, combining hand-laid fiberglass craftsmanship with factory-condition precision that is setting industry standards.

Why fiberglass?

• Fiberglass won't buckle, crack or break. With Colorado's expanding-contracting bentonite soil and temperamental weather, that's crucial.

• Fungus, algae, or loose dirt have little chance to grow on or adhere to the nonporous, chemically inert, seamless surface. Filters, vacuum cleaners and modern chemicals will keep your pool sparkling clean and its water pure.

• Fiberglass units are quick and easy to install, usually within a matter of days, not weeks.

The appealing design of these pools and spas is evident to more than 2,500 satisfied customers in the Rocky Mountain area. Incidentally, San Juan Pools and Spas received two major awards at the 1982 National Spa and Pool Institute's design competition—the equivalent to the movie industry's Academy Awards.

No wonder people are enjoying the privacy of their own pool or spa the San Juan way.

san juan pools & spas
Colorado-made Fiberglass

by

SWENSEN'S

2690 S. Havana
(Havana at Yale)
Aurora
751-9587

7301 W. Alameda
(across from Villa Italia)
Lakewood
232-1389

6911 S. University
(Southglenn Mall)
Littleton
795-3142

Remember the local drugstore when you were young? Remember the wire-backed chairs and marbletop tables?

Remember the banana splits with *real* ice cream topped with scoopfuls of syrup and gobs of crushed nuts? Remember Tiffany lamps and stained glass windows?

Like a set from "Hello, Dolly," Swensen's Ice Cream Parlors capture the flavor of those bygone days.

Speaking of flavor, Swensen's normally has up to 40 flavors to choose from. Apple, bordeaux cherry, carmel turtle fudge, sherbets, cinnamon crunch, peppermint stick, and Turkish coffee are just a few. *Real* ice cream!

All ingredients are fresh and natural. Juice, semitart strawberries, plump ripe bananas, chewy piquant black walnuts, firm red cherries.

Beware. Swensen's ice cream is rich. Outrageously rich! A single dip cone weighs a quarter-pound.

Throw caution to the wind. Try a Swensen's Earthquake Sundae—eight scoops of your choice of flavors topped generously with whipped cream, almonds and cherries. Your taste buds might register 8.9 on the Richter Scale by the time you're finished.

Some Swensen's locations also offer sandwiches, burgers, salads and quiche for your eating pleasure. All are prepared with the same care as their ice cream.

The Swensen's owners invite you to "come in for fun and a real treat. We'll make you happy."

APPLEJACK COUNTRY

3320 Youngfield
233-3331

A spirited encounter among friends is often heightened by the spirits being poured. The nature of the occasion determines the nature of the refreshment—a smooth cognac after a gourmet dinner while relaxing near the fireplace, for example, differs tremendously from the aperitif enjoyed after an evening at the symphony. The more one knows about fine wines and liquors, the easier the choices become. But where can a person find the exact selection desired under one roof?

There is a place.

Applejack Liquor in Wheat Ridge is America's single largest retail liquor market. With a sales floor the size of a football field, Applejack partner Alan Freis says, "There isn't an alcoholic beverage available in Colorado that we don't stock, including wines from almost every vineyard in the world and more than 100 domestic and imported beers."

The vast selection at Applejack is the result of careful planning by Freis and his two partners, Ozzie Malek and Bruce Paul. All three men had considerable experience before taking over the Applejack operation in 1980. Freis was the regional representative of Seagram Distillery for five years and a liquor wholesaler for six years. Malek had been involved in liquor wholesaling for 16 years. And Paul, a lawyer, brought his expertise in investments to the operation.

They know what the public wanted, as over 1 million customers last year can testify. A solid portion of the Applejack success story is due to the many special services they provide. Last year, for instance, they printed an oversized playing card (a jack, of course) that listed all the ski areas in Colorado and gave pertinent information about each area. The cards were mailed to the ski areas listed and to travel agencies in every state from Illinois to California. Since the Applejack store is conveniently located by I-70, many people took advantage of a discount coupon incorporated into the card as they drove into the mountain for a day on the slopes.

Other services include clinics on the

proper use of cordials in cooking and entertaining, and a recent exhibition by the Budweiser Clydesdale horses, which attracted 5,000 spectators who surely enjoyed the beer tapped from the Budweiser wagon.

For last year's holiday season, Applejack offered a "six pack" for the connoisseur who has everything. This extraordinary half-dozen bottles of distilled spirits included a 100 year old decanter of Hardy French Cognac, 25 year old Glenfiddich Scotch in a hand-cut crystal decanter, an 1882 bottle of Baron Louis de Rothschild mouton wine, a hand-cut Baccarat crystal decanter of Louis XIII cognac champagne, a giant salamanzar of Mumm's Cordon Rouge, and a rare bottle of Couvee Dom Perignon champagne. The package sold for just over $7,000 with free delivery by limousine. The special this coming holiday season promises to be just as spectacular.

So whether one is looking for an inexpensive beer to sip during the weekend TV sports marathons or a rare vintage wine for a grand celebration, Applejack Liquors has it all.

Boutique International Ltd.

**Larimer Square
1455 Larimer St.
629-6345**

A trip to Boutique International Ltd. at Larimer Square is as good as a trip around the world when you are looking for gifts for the people in your life.

In business since 1967, Boutique International imports items found nowhere else in Denver. Take handcrafted steins and nutcrackers for instance, or fur-felt Bittner hats from Austria.

Here you will find a magnificent line of European imports: Steinbock of Austria, Lodenfrey of Munich, Strasser of Germany, Lanz of Salzburg, Lodencoats, Dirndls, Jankers and casual clothing.

Why fly to England for Whitefriars full lead crystal paperweights, or jaunt to Denmark for fine silver? You can find it all at Boutique International.

Le Chocolat

**Larimer Square
1430 Larimer
623-2949**

Le Chocolat of Larimer Square is the fulfillment of every candy fantasy you've ever had, from the sublime to the ridiculous.

Inside its cozy confines, jars and trays and counters brim with domestic and imported licorice, jelly bellies, rock candy, jaw breakers, fudges, peanut brittle, holiday candies, and the always popular Larimer Square mints.

And the chocolate. Oh, the chocolate! Fine Swiss delights like Moreau and Tobler, Dutch chocolate, "After Eight" from England, and the store's own privately labeled chocolate. They sell singles in any chocolate, and they'll custom pack and gift wrap their goodies.

One devours this incredible sight amidst some of Denver's most historical decor. The candy counters come from the old Daniels and Fisher Building; the woodwork from the Windsor Hotel.

Le Chocolat has been owner-operated for fifteen years. They know their customers as well as they do their candies and chocolates.

Sweet dreams.

Mae Norcross Linens

255 Detroit
322-1613

What do formal dinners have in common with a luxurious bath and a good night's sleep?

They're all incredibly enriched by Mae Norcross Linens.

At Mae Norcross Linens you'll discover a superb collection of table linens, towels, and bedding, including baby blankets and pillows, down comforters, round bedding.

Dream on dreamy percale. Sample the best quilted placemats, hand-embroidered handkerchiefs, 100% cotton bedding.

Have you ever slipped between Egyptian cotton sheets? You'll never know how soft sleep can be until you do.

Luxurious? Definitely. Expensive? Naturally. But Mae Norcross carries linens and towels for every budget—from top-of-the-line such as Martex and Wamsutta, to the best buys in town.

And what you don't find, Mae Norcross can locate for you, because their specialized service is as distinctive as the merchandise they carry.

You can make these items even more distinctive by having Mae Norcross custom monogram your towels and linens.

Mae Norcross recently moved into a new, enlarged location next door to the Cherry Creek shop that carried these fine linens for over 18 years. Why not visit their new place and let Mae Norcross Linens put the little soft pleasures into your life.

WILLIAM ERNEST BROWN

Marina Square
8101 E. Belleview Ave.
771-2774

In this age of instant electronic communication it's easy to forget the pleasures and permanence of writing. But who could not be inspired to commit their best thoughts to paper with elegant stationery from William Ernest Brown?

Letters, billet-doux, invitations, and thank-you notes will more closely reflect your precise sentiments when you choose from this stationery salon's marvelous collection of beautiful papers. The designs vary from the whimsical and witty to elegant, custom creations—all bearing taste and imagination.

Owners Marilyn Gage and Nancy Shwayder, in keeping with the other exclusive William Ernest Brown stores across the country, display and treat their custom social stationery, along with desk accessories and party accoutrements, like fine jewelry.

They carry only the best lines, always with new and different merchandise. Papers by Crane, Consortium, and Georges Lalo; desk sets by Jeffrey Benjamin; leather by Alicia Kempner; address books by Helene Batoff.

But Marilyn and Nancy particularly enjoy special projects. Sit down with them for an after-hours appointment in their cozy, living room setting. They'll help you create custom invitations and announcements, design corporate gifts in leather and brass, select desk accessories to match your decor, and help you find just the right wording for invitations.

Says Marilyn: "We get comments every day: how glad our clients are that Denver finally has a store like ours . . . that they used to get their stationery in Chicago or New York . . . and that it just makes them feel good to come in and browse."

Esprit du Soleil

Esprit du Soleil
1067 Old South Gaylord
722-4791

Paper and Pen Shop
1045 Old South Gaylord
722-2100

Upstairs/Downstairs
1061 Old South Gaylord
778-0826

Definitely not to be missed . . . the all-embracing "spirit of the sun" that permeates Greig and Nancy Thomson's three distinctive shops along Denver's Old South Gaylord!

Country prints charming by Pierre Deux, imported exclusively in Colorado from France, abound in stunning wonderments like handbags, tabletop linens, picture frames and such. Pretty things from Pierre's folkloric French countryside—to tote, tuck and treasure. French too: the luxury of silken body scents by Roger and Gallet.

Viva la France, but that's just the beginning! At the hands of these two gifted American designers, a luxe assemblage of creative ideas has been collected in truly uncommon surroundings: silk flowers in interesting containers, ceramic and china vessels and sculpture in unusual shapes, faience in irresistible colors and themes. Charming, deftly selected country furniture . . . fine old pine cupboards, chairs, tables and trestles: some are endearingly flourished with original motifs by artist Nancy Backus Thomson.

Daughters Lucy and Virginia, talented Thomsons too, preside over the newest offspring of Esprit du Soleil: *Paper and Pen,* and *Upstairs/Downstairs.*

In the Paper and Pen shop, the art of writing letters to friends is revived among exquisite Il Papiro Italian hand-marbled papers and accessories; names like Crane . . . and other fine stationeries in every hue imaginable, to buy by the sheet or by the pound. Instruments and inks go from appropriate to surprising! Specialized greeting cards and wrapping papers for all occasions, formal to whimsical, simply cannot be found anywhere else.

Upstairs/Downstairs is exactly what one might expect . . . the unexpected! A potpourri of favorite things, where one can let one's imagination run wild: here, a niche of old-fashioned colored bottles with wired, rubbered tops, in all sizes and shapes, destined to be heirlooms; there, on the floor and up the walls and hanging from the ceiling, a fine collection of earthy cooking accoutrements fit for your favorite chef . . . perhaps it's you? There are baskets and puppets and pots and country linens. It's a fairyland of change . . . yet all three shops retain the inimitable signature of their talented founders.

RON JOHNSON/IMAGEWORKS

450-8041

Give your old wall a new face. One-of-a-kind ceramic faces from Masquerade can turn a mundane wall into one hard to ignore.

These wall hangings, a unique blend of art and interior design, are quite unlike anything you've ever seen. Owners Peggy and Penny McConnell have created hand-painted, three-dimensional masks embellished with quality fabrics, silk flowers, genuine furs, antique baubles, feathers and other touches for an unexpected composite of textures.

Dictated by style or period, these pieces range from subtly elegant to whimsical. Art Deco, Art Nouveau, Victorian and other period pieces radiate the elemental richness of a romantic age. Japanese Kabuki masks capture the exotic Orient. Jesters, clowns, and Pierrots enliven a room with drama. Diversity of design is also expressed in Avant Garde geometric painting, the integration of neon, as well as other delightful materials.

Accessorizing with masks enables one to create a special ambience complimenting collectibles. The versatility of any piece can afford lasting pleasure.

Make a discriminating statement to suit your lifestyle.

Consultation with the designers determines your particular interests in color, period, style, and integration with decor. Masquerade offers a gallery of faces at affordable prices, or faces can be commissioned for your personal specifications.

Faces designed to turn heads.

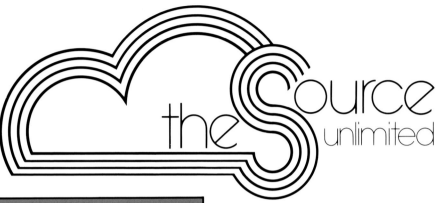

the Source unlimited

Cherry Creek North
300 Fillmore St.
333-0900

Accessories are special touches that give character and life to a home. A saucy piece of brass, a reliable antique, a delicate figurine, a brilliant piece of crystal, can establish the ambience of a room and speak volumes of its owners.

With that in mind, the selection of accessories takes on ever greater importance. At The Source Unlimited, owners Steve Powell and Dennis Clark provide an eclectic variety of beautiful items to choose from, a veritable Nieman-Marcus gallery, as well as expert counsel on how best to integrate accessories naturally into your specific settings.

For the animal lover, The Source Unlimited has an excellent selection of animal sculptures, up to life-size, including signed, limited-edition bronze deers from Thailand. How about an antique Coromandel screen or Imari fruit box? Fine prints for the walls?

Did someone say shells? Shells, shells, shells of all kinds, at all prices, are at The Source Unlimited. Nobody in Denver can match this exciting collection of shells from around the world.

"People like nature," says Steve, "and the shells and natural mineral specimens represent nature in its most symmetrical beauty."

The Source Unlimited helps you decide what to choose by displaying these items in dozens of lovely vignettes. Of course, the complete design service at The Source Unlimited provides a coherent approach to decorating that will help you create that special character you want to convey.

Entertainment & Leisure

Ancient animals and modern art. Learning exhibits for children and the stars for adults. Colorado history and Asian textiles. Whatever interests you and your family have, you'll find exciting things to see and do among the following pages.

McNichols Sports Arena could be called the Proteus of Denver's events centers. In any given week the huge arena may change forms to host a professional hockey game, a statewide political convention, a pop concert, a religious meeting and a soccer match. ⟍ Part of Denver's convention complex, McNichols is the city's newest and largest indoor facility. Its fixed seating can accommodate 16,500 spectators, and another 2,500 portable seats can be added for such events as concerts and conventions. The arena is named for Mayor William H. McNichols, under whose administration this $10 million sports and entertainment complex was built in 1975. Since its opening, an annual average of 1½ million people have pushed through its turnstiles. ⟍ McNichols is home to three major sports franchises: the Denver Nuggets (professional basketball); Colorado Rockies (professional hockey); and the Denver Avalanche (professional indoor soccer). Though ostensibly a sports center, McNichols is also one of the city's entertainment showcases. Shows and concerts by The Who, Willie Nelson, the Ice Capades, John Denver, and The Police have entertained McNichols audiences. In fact, the first public event at the arena was a sell out concert by Lawrence Welk and his orchestra. ⟍ If you're new to the Mile-High City, you may sometimes hear Denverites refer to McNichols in another, more colloquial way, a moniker that came into vogue about the time a particular hamburger became popular. And from a distance, this huge, circular, sleek structure does indeed bear a striking resemblance to a Big Mac.

denver's ZOO

City Park
575-2754

Open every day of the year at
10:00 a.m.-5:00 p.m. winter
10:00 a.m.-6:00 p.m. summer

Admission:
$3 — Adults
$1 — Children 6-15
$1 — Seniors 65 and older
Free — Children under 6

For most of us city-bound folks a zoo is our strongest link to wildlife. Not many of us will ever travel to the Sumatra rain forest to glimpse an orangutan or to the Arctic to observe a polar bear.

Consequently, fostering concern and appreciation for wildlife and its natural habitat has long been a major emphasis of the Denver Zoo, one of the oldest American zoos west of the Mississippi and a major attraction of the Rocky Mountain region. The zoo's 1,500 specimens represent nearly 400 species and include many rare and endangered animal species. They give living testament to the natural world around us and to the crucial need to preserve adequate wild spaces.

The Denver Zoo accents this need with its use of spacious, barless enclosures, which approximate natural habitats for the animals. An early innovative example of this is the realistic manmade rock formations of Bear Mountain, constructed in 1918, which dis-plays polar and grizzly bears and several California sea lions.

Among the zoo's many other exhibits, all designed to accommodate handicapped visitors, are the feline house, the mountain habitat of rarely exhibited Dall and Rocky Mountain Bighorn sheep, and the delightful Monkey Island (not open in the winter). Not to be missed is Bird World, one of the finest exhibits for birds in the United States, with its walk-through tropical rain forest and the popular hummingbird jungle.

In the belief that wildlife education begins with the young, the Denver Zoo has a particularly active program for children in grades one through twelve. On specially guided learning safaris children study animal adaptation, endangered species, behavior, and the need to preserve wild spaces. Children also have their own special zoo for close contact with a variety of domestic and exotic animals.

A rubber-tired train, the Zoo-liner, makes periodic forays to all these exhibits, which are set in park-like surroundings. A gift and souvenir shop is located at the zoo, as well as several refreshment stands and a restaurant.

The zoo performs many functions—recreation, conservation, and research—but none is more crucial than education. And education costs money. Think of all the mouths the zoo has to feed. So don't just visit the Denver Zoo. Join it!

THE DENVER ART MUSEUM

100 West 14th Avenue Parkway
Denver, Colorado 80204
303/575-2793

Tues.-Sat. 10 a.m.-4:30 p.m.
Wed. 10 a.m. - 8 p.m.
Sun. 1 p.m.-5 p.m.
Closed Monday and major holidays

If Denver can rightly be called the gateway to the Rockies, the Denver Art Museum is certainly the gateway to the world.

Where else in town can you travel across continents, leap back through time, dip into fascinating cultures—all in a single place?

Housed in a dramatic, seven-story building downtown, the Denver Art Museum holds some 30,000 objects, and has a gift shop and book store, as well as a fine restaurant. It is the largest art museum between Kansas City and the West Coast and one of the finest art museums in America.

While you can experience the art of virtually any nation at the museum, you might want to start with the Native Arts collection. This collection is recognized as one of the foremost in the world with clothing, bead work, basketry, sand painting, and jewelry representing the arts of Native American and Eskimo tribes

Do you have a passion for European art? Degas, Monet, Corot, Picasso? Or Asian art? The museum displays paintings, sculptures, ceramics, and an extensive collection of Hindu, Buddhist, and Islamic religious objects.

There are intriguing collections of textiles and costumes, art of the New World from pre-Columbian through the 19th century, and a fine assembly of American art.

The museum's personable staff is always available to provide directions, advice, and insight into the beauty and significance of the museum's pieces.

In an endeavor to provide painless education for its patrons, the museum presents a highly successful lecture-of-the-month series, musical and cultural events tied to specific showings, travel programs, films, children's classes, and school touring programs.

And ARTREK, the museum's traveling exhibition van, roams the state, bringing objects from the marvelous collection to large and small communities.

Visit the Denver Art Museum. Better yet, become a member. Help support the place that can put you within arm's length of the world.

Denver Botanic Gardens

1005 York St.
575-2548

Many people think of the Denver Botanic Gardens as the imposing conservatory at 10th and York that houses a myriad of exotic tropical and subtropical plants. But in 1981 more than 200,000 visitors learned that it is much more—it is a place where not only plants, but also people, grow.

One tour through the Denver Botanic Gardens is enough to convince anyone that love of plants and flowers is not required to appreciate the remarkable experience this facility provides.

True, the conservatory and the Boettcher Memorial Center, with its library, lecture hall, and gift shop, are the heart and nerve center of the Botanic Gardens, but most of its 18 acres are devoted to outdoor attractions. With more than two dozen specific areas of interest, it is impossible to catalog all of them. We offer a brief sampling:

The Gates Memorial Garden—one of the first plantings after the Botanic Gardens was established. It simulates a Rocky Mountain landscape combining native plants, trees, shrubs and ground cover along with a stream, waterfall and rocky cliffs.

Shofu-en, The Garden of Pine Wind—an intimate garden where gnarled pine trees grow along peaceful waterways. From the tea house, one can overlook the iris-bordered pond, and truly imagine being transported to a tranquil spot in Japan.

The Scripture Garden—an inspiring, contemplative setting of native sandstone and exotic plant life, which features a bronze mosaic sculpture combining symbols of the Christian and Jewish faiths.

The Denver Botanic Gardens offers more than sensual pleasure. Founded in 1951, it remains dedicated to its original goals: to collect, preserve, cultivate and display plants, flowers, shrubs and trees; to advance botanical and horticultural knowledge through education, research and experimentation; to encourage gardening and horticulture by providing classes, lectures, workshops and film programs in addition to tours and exhibitions.

The Denver Botanic Gardens is open 363 days of the year from 9 A.M. to 4:45 P.M. A modest fee is charged for non-members. The Gardens, only partially funded by the city, welcomes tax-exempt contributions and memberships. Phone 575-2548 to request a colorful membership brochure describing the Gardens and its programs.

City Park
575-3872

Hours: Mon.-Sat. 9 a.m.-4:30 p.m.
Sun. 12 p.m.-4:30 p.m.
Closed: Jan. 1, Thanks-
giving, Dec, 24, 25, 31

Admission: $2.00 Adults
$1.00 Seniors, 62 and over
$ .75 Children under 16
Free to members and
children under six

MUSEUM OF NATURAL HISTORY

In the midst of a concrete and glass city growing rapidly into the future, it's easy to forget our past and concentrate only on the present. The Denver Museum of Natural History provides a fresh and striking reminder of man's heritage and the natural world around him.

For instance, the museum's exhibits of North American natives feature the contributions of the American Indian. The dioramas of rare South American animals speak of the rich diversity and complexity of the natural world today. And the fossilized skeletons in the Dinosaur Hall remind us of the fate of those who fail to adapt to change.

Opened in 1908, the Denver Museum of Natural History has gained an international reputation for the quality of its exhibits, particularly its 75 life-size ecological habitat dioramas that show in remarkable detail animals from around the world in their natural environments. The Botswana Africa Hall, for example, is the only one of its kind in the Northern Hemisphere and includes one of the largest dioramas in the world.

The three floors of the museum contain more than 400 other displays of anthropology, gems, paleobotany, cetaceans, birds and mammals. Of special interest to Coloradans are eleven major exhibits pertaining to Colorado's five Life Zones, as well as the Coors Mineral Hall that emphasizes the state's native minerals. Its collection of crystallized leaf gold from Breckenridge is the finest in the world.

Any good museum is a living, growing institution, and Denver's museum is no exception. Its active series of traveling exhibits, lectures, film shows, tours, demonstrations and workshops keeps visitors up to date on the latest findings of anthropologists, paleontologists and naturalists.

Little wonder that the Denver Museum of Natural History is the city's biggest attraction. Located in the beautiful City Park, it is accessible to the handicapped and it contains a snack bar, rest areas, and gift and book shops. It also houses the popular Gates Planetarium which takes audiences on simulated trips to our own solar system and beyond.

MELANIE EVE BAROCAS

931 Bannock St.
571-5198

Imagine . . .

Picture a child allaying his fears of the dentist by playing with a working dental chair. Imagine children coming to a better understanding of handicaps by taking a "blind walk" and trying out a wheelchair. Envision kids learning about TV news by working with actual TV equipment in a simulated TV station.

These are a few of the many changing exhibits for children ages 3-13 at the remarkable Children's Museum. No "hands off" warnings or sterile glass cases here. Instead, children explore, discover and learn while having fun.

The Children's Museum has a theater, in which performances for children take place on weekends. The Museum also publishes a variety of family publications, including *Boing*, a children's newspaper, which is distributed to schools nationwide. It also offers participatory traveling exhibits to schools, shopping centers, and other museums.

The Children's Museum. A world designed for children.

Imagine that.

the children's museum

Call for information and hours:
320-0120

Now the stars are as accessible as Denver's fabled mountains. Crossing the Milky Way is as simple as crossing town to the Charles C. Gates Planetarium in City Park.

Visitors to the planetarium may be whisked away to the rosy plains of Mars, through the swirling gravitational whirlpool of a black hole, or even into the fiery heart of the sun—all without leaving the comforts of the planetarium chamber.

Hundreds of visitors each day learn the mysteries of space under a 50-foot dome that seems to magically disappear into the infinite blackness of the heavens. Each program utilizes the latest NASA photos and astronomical discoveries. Original art work may depict life on other worlds, or reveal forming galaxies, dying stars and other cosmic events. Scores of special effects projectors (some programs require more than 200) are designed and built by planetarium technicians to illustrate the sometimes violent, sometimes mysterious and always beautiful world of astronomy.

And backing up each thought-provoking and easy to understand script is the stereophonic sound of specially commissioned original music and effects.

But the highlight of every show is a sophisticated electronic space simulator located in the center of the chamber. Thousands of stars and other cosmic phenomena produce a highly realistic illusion of gazing into the night sky or flying through the realms of deep space.

Gates Planetarium also offers laser light and music concerts. Laser shows simply must be experienced, not conveyed by the limitations of words.

A fully stocked planetarium shop features hundreds of astronomical books, posters, science fiction records and other souvenirs. Fine astronomical telescopes also are for sale.

Hours and topics vary during the year, so it's best to call first for program information. Gates Planetarium is located within the Denver Museum of Natural History at Montview and Colorado Boulevard.

GATES PLANETARIUM

MAMMOTH GARDENS

1510 Clarkson Street
831-4068

Mammoth Gardens, that behemoth building on Clarkson just off Colfax in Historic Capitol Hill, has been renovated into a multi-use facility unlike any other establishment in the country.

The heart of Mammoth Gardens is a 35,000 square-foot hall adaptable to conventions, concerts, sporting events, trade shows, banquets or any activity that requires vast floor space. Mammoth provides in-house catering for up to 2,000 people and can seat over 3,000 sports fans or concertgoers. The Uptown Restaurant and Bar overlooking the central arena features one of Denver's most unique and popular menus.

Among the events held at Mammoth since its opening in September 1982 have been a Sunday afternoon winefest for 3,000 patrons of Denver's public television station; a reception for singer Willie Nelson, sponsored by the Denver International Film Festival and attended by several thousand fans; a fund-raising event for Colorado Governor Dick Lamm; the Rocky Mountain Marine Boat Show; qualifying rounds for the United Bank Tennis Classic; and an assortment of jazz, rock and classical music concerts.

Built in 1907 as a roller skating rink, Mammoth Gardens has been used as a manufacturing plant for the Fritchle Electric Car, a hall for dance marathons during the Great Depression, an ice skating arena and a sports center during the Second World War. Many Denverites fondly recall the fun and camaraderie of roller skating at Mammoth during the Forties and Fifties.

After languishing through much of the Sixties, Mammoth's doors were once again opened to the public in the Seventies when the facility became a concert hall for the nation's top rock bands. It was an on-again-off-again operation through the mid-70s, when a new concept was developed that would open Mammoth as a multi-use events and entertainment center. That idea caught on, funding was found, renovations undertaken, and Mammoth Gardens found new life again.

Mammoth Gardens today is the product of an urban renaissance in the last seven years as people have rediscovered the usefulness and beauty of our historic buildings. Mammoth is an example of what private enterprise can do for urban redevelopment.

The newfound popularity of Mammoth Gardens is best illustrated by the fact that the facility has events booked well into 1983. The old behemoth is ready and able to serve the Denver community in a spirited, contemporary way!

UNIVERSITY OF COLORADO MUSEUM

492-6165 during week
492-6892 weekends

Weekdays 9-5 Sat. 9-4 Sun. 10-4

Did you know—
—That Boulder now stands on land once covered by the sea?
—That agriculture came to Colorado 2,000 years ago?
—That the front range structure is 70 million years old?

Many such interesting facts about Colorado and the Rocky Mountain region can be found at the University of Colorado Museum, founded more than 75 years ago to contribute to our knowledge of the flora and fauna, the ecology, natural features, archaeology, ethnology, history, and arts of the region.

Displayed in permanent and changing exhibits, these collections, many donated by area residents, contain specimens from around the world. The museum's fossil mollusks, for instance, have attracted scholars from as far away as Japan. Its kachina doll collection is world-recognized. Its McKenna Room exhibits fine ethnographic art.

The exhibit halls include a Hall of Earth with permanent exhibits of minerals, rocks, and fossils illustrating local geologic features; the Hall of Life, depicting some of the basic concepts of biology; the Hall of Humanity, showing how cultures evolve and change through time, with a special emphasis on the archaeology of the southwestern United States; and the newest area in the museum, the Gallery.

The Gallery is the site of many changing exhibitions that expand the normal boundaries of natural history. Regularly featured are exhibitions of Oriental art from the collections of Denver connoisseur, H. Medill Sarkisian, who has amassed one of the country's finest private collections of Asian textiles, paintings, ceramics, bronzes, and other *objets d'art.* Past exhibits in the Gallery also include historic Navajo and Pueblo Indian weaving curated by anthropologist Joe Ben Wheat; an amazing variety of insects and their unique lifestyles, organized by entomologist Url Lanham; the timeless beauty of fossils, discovered in bone and shell and coordinated by paleontologist Judith Harris.

Because of the Museum's particular emphasis on teaching and research at the university level, many more of the collections are not regularly on display. These study collections can be viewed by prearranged tour with the curators.

Unique approaches to interpreting the world around us form a part of the Museum's ongoing program to convey what university museum research is all about—to educate *and* to enthuse.

The Colorado Heritage Center
1300 Broadway
866-4591

COLORADO HISTORICAL SOCIETY

The Colorado Historical Society, founded in 1879, is a state educational institution dedicated to collecting, preserving, and interpreting the history and the prehistory of Colorado.

Housing the $20 million collection of historic and prehistoric artifacts and documents, the Heritage Center contains exhibition galleries, educational classrooms, library research facilities, historic preservation and archaeology functions, and Society administration offices.

The Society maintains 16 museums and historic properties throughout the state, five of them in the Denver metropolitan area.

Colorado Heritage Center, 1300 Broadway, Denver. Among the exhibits are Mesa Verde artifacts, a timeline of Colorado and world events, pioneer photographer W.H. Jackson, silver king H.A.W. Tabor, childhood in Colorado, the dioramas, and a variety of other subjects. Special history exhibits are offered on a changing basis.
Hours: Monday to Friday, 9 am to 5 pm; Saturday, Sunday, and holidays, 10 am to 5 pm; closed Christmas Day.
Admission: a fee is charged.
Information: 866-3682

Grant-Humphreys Mansion, 770 Pennsylvania Street, Denver. This turn-of-the-century residence of two leading Colorado families has been preserved and is used as office and public space, the latter part of which is available for tours and private rental functions.
Hours: Monday to Friday, 10 am to 3 pm.
Admission: a fee is charged.
Information: 866-3507

Pearce-McAllister Cottage, 1880 Gaylord Street, Denver. Built in 1899 in the Dutch Colonial Revival style, this house reflects Colorado growth through the life of Harold Pearce and Henry McAllister, who were active in mining, railroading, trading, and investing.
Hours: Sunday and Wednesday, 1 to 4 pm.
Admission: a fee is charged.
Information: 866-3682

Georgetown Loop Historic Mining Area, 50 miles west of Denver, in Georgetown. Train rides on the narrow-gauge Georgetown Loop and tours of the Lebanon Silver Mine tell the story of 19th century railroading and mining in Colorado.
Hours: Daily from Memorial Day to Labor Day, 10 am to 4 pm.
Admission: fees are charged for the train ride and mine tour.
Information: 279-6101 (Denver) and 569-2403 (Georgetown)

Boulder Center for the Visual Arts
1750 13th St.
Boulder
443-2122

Back in the early Seventies, the arts center now known as the Boulder Center for the Visual Arts was located in a Victorian house. It was more of a club then, comprised of artists, patrons, and others who believed that art was to be shared with each other and the community.

Today the BCVA is located in a newer, larger building with impressive exhibits by exciting artists. But the philosophy remains the same. At BCVA, art is still something to be shared.

The focus of that shared purpose is local and regional contemporary art, and the BCVA has become recognized throughout the region for its commitment to that goal.

The Boulder Center presents a mix of single artist, juried, and invitational shows, along with national exhibitions and first-rate traveling shows. Photography, watercolors, sculptures, paintings, and prints are among the arts exhibited.

BCVA acts as catalyst and liaison between the community and the arts, sponsoring lectures, classes, arts publications, poetry readings, workshops, and receptions. It hosts community arts groups and appropriate performing arts events.

The Boulder Center for the Visual Arts hopes you'll join this exciting alliance with the arts. As a BCVA member you'll receive a newsletter, special admittance to events, and you'll be able to attend the many openings and meet the artists themselves.

Resorts & Travel

One can't help thinking of Denver without thinking of outstanding resorts and adventurous travel. Crisp powder skiing, exhilarating mountain hikes, photographic vistas around every turn. Let Denver Now be your road map to the best in resorts and travel.

On a clear day, with a long, single sweep of the eyes, one can lay claim to the Front Range of the Colorado Rockies from Pikes Peak 60 miles south of Denver to Long's Peak 50 miles to the north. ⤷ It is a panorama of splendor and promise. ⤷ To the newcomer, the 65-million-year-old peaks appear to rise almost mystically out of dry plains; to the natives and others of long standing, the Front Range holds out the prospect of rejuvenation and eternity. ⤷ These are mountains of mercurial moods. On a winter's morn the snow-capped peaks glow pink. On a summer's eve the serrated edges turn deep purple. Warm chinooks hurtle unexpectedly down the canyons. Thunderstorms spill violently over the edge. ⤷ Yet the Front Range is much more than a place of grandeur and legend and temperament. It is the source of life for Denver, for the communities that have sprawled hungrily at its feet. It was the gold veins of the mountains that lured the prospectors who founded Denver in 1858. Later, the gold was replaced by silver, by the black gold of oil and coal, and the white gold of skiing. ⤷ The Front Range is the eastern face of a mountain backbone 300 miles deep, providing Denver with its most precious commodity of all, water, enabling the metropolitan area to mushroom to nearly two million people. ⤷ The Front Range gave birth to Denver, nurtured her growth, and shaped much of the city's character. The mountains have lifted spirits, inspired dreams, created destinies. Their elemental ruggedness has forever ingrained our city with a rough-hewn streak that refuses to be erased by our increasing cosmopolitanism. ⤷ Denver. The "Queen City of the Plains" she may be. But her spirit belongs to the mountains.

CLUB MED®
"The Antidote for Civilization"

If you believe a vacation should be a total escape from the pressures and routines of daily living, why not get above it all? Escape to the top of Copper Mountain in Colorado, where Club Mediterranee has opened its first vacation village in the United States.

Perched near the summit of Colorado's exquisite high country, only 75

miles west of Denver, Copper Mountain's Franco-American village beckons all who know that the combination of Colorado skiing and Club Med is the closest thing to Nirvana.

No wonder skiers from around the world come here to experience the crisp blue skies, taste Colorado's "champagne" air, and feel their skis carve effortlessly through the deep powder snow.

For the alpine skiers, Copper Mountain offers 40 miles of runs over 48 trails, with a variety of challenging runs designed for beginners, intermediates, and advanced. Nine double chairlifts, one Poma, and one enclosed double chairlift run from the 9,600-foot base anywhere up to the 12,050-foot summit.

If you wish to sharpen your skiing techniques, take lessons from one of our expert instructors. You'll be evaluated and placed with skiers of similar abilities. And you'll stay with the same ski instructor for the entire week. In addition, most classes are videotaped for you to see precisely what skills you need to improve.

As at all Club Med winter villages, lift passes and instruction are part of your vacation package. So enjoy unlimited skiing every day of your stay, except on arrival day.

If you prefer to touch nature, why not try cross-country skiing along Copper's 22 miles of well-marked trails? Instructors can help beginners become proficient in just a few days. Experienced cross-country devotees can explore the more remote countryside, and can picnic at one of the most spectacular spots this side of the Alps.

For the youngsters five to twelve, a mini club offers special ski classes morning and afternoon, while well-trained counselors provide supervision and fun throughout the day. And remember, whether you ski cross-country or downhill, there is a rental shop at the village offering the finest ski equipment at a nominal fee.

If skiing is not your fancy, consider ice skating at a nearby lighted outdoor pond (outside the club at an extra cost), play ping-pong or chess, take bridge or French/English language lessons, practice yoga, go shopping at our village boutique. Or just walk and enjoy some of the cleanest, most invigorating climate in the world.

After a hard day's play in this winter wonderland, relax in our Jacuzzis and saunas. Meet with some of your new international friends for a drink at the bar or around the cozy stone fireplace. Enjoy dinner overlooking the slopes you just conquered.

Listen to recorded classical music concerts at sunset. Go dancing till dawn or take in the evening cabaret put on by our own talented staff.

Or step outside and catch the mountains in moonlight.

Copper Mountain is an impressive addition to Club Med's incomparable string of 88 "vacation villages" located in 26 countries around the world. Guests can unwind among the secluded bougainvillea of Playa Blanca in Mexico, ride horseback through the rolling green hillsides of Pompadour in central France, or catch the warm caress of the ocean at Bora Bora in French Polynesia.

The magic of these mini-Utopias is inherent in the philosophy that has guided Club Med since its inception 32 years ago. Simply put, our philosophy is that vacations and the everyday world shouldn't mix. That's why each village is self-contained, usually in isolated, natural surroundings, a buffer against the harried, frazzled world you left behind.

From the moment you arrive at any Club village you'll discover that those familiar barriers, rules, and inhibitions of society melt away. Friendships blossom at a single greeting. Tensions slip away on the breezes. Casualness overtakes you. No need for fancy wardrobes at Club Med. No telephones or alarm clocks jangle. No television or radios or newspapers intrude.

As in any Utopia, a Club village is a cashless society. Check your wallet and your financial worries at the desk upon your arrival. With the exception of drinks at the bar (paid for with multicolored poppet beads) and personal expenses at the boutique or on optional excursions, everything is prepaid. Your package includes hotel room or bungalow, all meals (scrumptious, overflowing buffets at breakfast and lunch, and a five-course feast at dinner), unlimited use of the extensive sports facilities and equipment, and expert sports instruction. And the wine's on us at lunch and dinner.

No unpleasant surprises here, just the surprise of learning how joyous a vacation can be.

Helping create that special feeling of pampered self-containment at our villages is our staff, who live, work, and play right alongside you. We think of them as hosts, not employees. In fact, we call them "G.O. s," initials for the French phrase *gentils organisateurs*, or nice organizers. Tipping is prohibited at all Club villages. One tips bellhops, not hosts.

When you're not playing and laughing with our G.O.s, you'll find a wonderfully cosmopolitan milieu of club members like yourself. Singles, married couples, single parents, and families, from their early 20s to their late 60s, flock to our far flung locations. Children six and up are welcome at most villages. And select villages provide special facilities for kids four and older.

Sports abound at our Mexican villages, favorite destinations for Coloradans. For instance, Ixtapa near Zihua-

CLUB MED.

tanejo hugs the edge of the blue Pacific, and offers among a multitude of possibilities tennis, free golf at its fabulous Robert Trent Jones Jr. course, windsurfing, and picnics on a secluded off-shore island. Another Colorado favorite is Playa Blanca, also on the Pacific. Scuba diving, deep sea fishing, horseback riding along the beach and mountain trails, and an evening of folklore are just a few of the activities to lure cosmopolitan dreamers.

So the next time you go on vacation, forget the world. But don't forget Club Med.

Club Med Villages in the Western Hemisphere

Mexico
Ixtapa
Playa Blanca
Cancun

The Bahamas
Paradise Island
Eleuthera

United States
Copper Mountain/Colorado

Tahiti
Moorea
Bora Bora

The Caribbean
Magic Haiti/Haiti
Punta Cana/Dominican Republic
Caravelle/Guadeloupe
Fort Royal/Guadeloupe
Buccaneer's Creek/Martinique

100 miles west of Denver on I-70
VailWatch 476-4888
1/800-525-3875

A great actor once said that American traditions are established quickly, where popular instinct and sentiment pronounce them sound.

Vail is such an American tradition. A mountain wilderness just a generation ago, Vail today is an unquestioned leader in world-class resorts.

It began as the vision of several World War II veterans who had trained in the Gore Valley for harsh fighting in the Italian Alps. Members of the 10th returned to the area after the war with plans to build a year 'round mountain resort. Ground was broken in 1961; Bavarian-style architecture ruled the designs of lodges, restaurants, and shops. Carefully designed ski runs were created on the surrounding slopes. A gondola lift was installed for summer use. The best restaurateurs from Europe and America moved to the fledgling community. As the town of Vail grew, so did its reputation as a first-class international resort.

Today Vail features more than 260 restaurants, lodges, shops and professional services of all descriptions. Miles of hiking and walking trails weave through the surrounding White River National Forest. There are 50 tennis courts, four championship 18-hole golf courses, the Colorado Ski Museum and the Vail Nature Center, movie theatres, night clubs, nearby facilities for fishing, camping, horseback riding, ice skating, bicycling—and the list goes on.

The resort features a variety of special events throughout the year. In the summer, the internationally respected Vail Institute sponsors a variety of programs such as symphony, dance and theatre. On the lighter side, the Vail Rugby Club and the Vail Soccer Team can always be counted on to provide a rambunctious afternoon's entertainment. Vail is the site of the Jerry Ford Invitational Golf Tournament and the Coors Bicycle Classic. Fall is the time for Vailfest, a Colorado version of the Bavarian Oktoberfest. And in the winter, skiing dominates, with world-class racers lounging at fireside with amateurs who can barely handle a snowplow turn without toppling over.

To help make the fun more accessible, Vail Resort Association has a central reservation system, and the town fathers furnish visitors with free transportation anywhere within city limits. Vail is indeed an all-season resort community dedicated to play and pleasure at any time of year.

COPPER MOUNTAIN

P.O. Box 3001
Copper Mountain, CO 80443
668-2882

A perfect ski mountain looms above, silhouetted snow white against the dense black blanket of the night. A cozy village, twinkling lights and drifting smoke, dozes contentedly in the pre-dawn morning. Copper Mountain, once an unknown wilderness inhabited by elk and Indians, today is one of the top ten ski resorts in North America.

Come ski Copper Mountain and discover what the U.S. Forest Service called "the most nearly perfect ski mountain in the United States." You'll find the winter days teeming with life as more than 10,000 skiers daily ride the lifts servicing Copper Mountain's 725 acres of exhilarating skiing. Fifty-one carefully sculpted trails guide visitors from east to west on the giant north-facing mountain. One-quarter of the trails, located on the eastern edge of the resort, are designated expert. Fifty percent of the trails are intermediate, and the remaining slopes, on the west side of the mountain, are for beginning skiers and cruisers.

Copper Mountain's master-planned village offers accommodations of every variety, from hotel rooms to luxury three-bedroom condominiums, all within walking distance of the lifts. You'll want to try ice skating on the lighted lake and explore the crisp, quiet world of cross-country skiing on 35 kilometers of maintained trails, too.

More than a dozen restaurants and shops of all kinds are just minutes from your condominium door. You can dine in candlelight or disco till midnight, or just stay home and cook up a feast of your own creation. Whether it's gourmet or guacamole, tacos or steak teriyaki, a popular dance floor or a soothing Jacuzzi. . . Copper Mountain has it all.

Beneath Copper Mountain's snow-covered slopes a summer of surprises awaits. The alpine breezes keep you cool while you enjoy your favorite sport, be it tennis, golf, horseback riding, hiking, fishing, biking, or running. Plenty of weekend activities add to the fun, with special events featuring road races, barbecues, a concert on the green from the Colorado Philharmonic and more. Craft fairs, antique displays, jazz festivals and fall color days add to the selections.

For the business-minded, a meeting or convention can be held at Copper Mountain amidst all the summer splendor of the Rocky Mountains. Facilities for small meetings or larger gatherings with full convention services are available, geared to your specific meeting needs.

This year come to Copper Mountain . . . Whether you want to ski at one of the best-designed ski areas in the west, or enjoy the cool beauty of a Colorado summer, Copper Mountain has it all

Beaver Creek™

P.O. Drawer 915
Avon, CO 81620
For information call:
303/949-6400 or
1/800-525-2257, toll free

When you arrive in Beaver Creek you'll find a community that is planned to stay active all year. You'll be able to ski a spectacular mountain on fine Colorado snow, golf on a Robert Trent Jones II golf course, play tennis, go hiking, explore a quaint village with exclusive boutiques and restaurants to suit any taste, or relax in comfortable lodging.

The extensive recreation facilities come first. The mountain sports seven chair lifts serving 560 acres of skiing that cater to every ability level. An 18-hole championship golf course opens to public play in June, 1982, with a complete pro shop and instruction program. Tennis courts are to be nestled in the valley for daily play and the spectacular back country beckons hikers and walkers. The reception center houses a model of what is to come in the community and offers an informative multi-image slide show.

Accommodations are available in lodge rooms, condominiums and townhouses offering such amenities as saunas, jacuzzis, restaurants and lounges, 24-hour room service and underground parking. There are rooms for meetings of 10 to 1,000 people.

A limited number of home sites are available, each giving owners seclusion and luxury and a personalized lifestyle. Once in Beaver Creek, people begin to relax as the mountain environment overtakes the pace of everyday life. Guests can reach Beaver Creek from Denver by car on I-70 or on Rocky Mountain Airways to the Avon STOL-port, landing practically at the gateway to the resort.

winter park ®

P.O. Box 36
Winter Park, CO 80482
Denver direct 892-0961

Winter Park is Denver's year 'round backyard playground.

Skiing, of course, is what Winter Park is most famous for. One of the oldest and largest ski areas in the state, Winter Park is the closest major ski resort to Denver.

Actually, Winter Park embraces two distinct ski areas: the legendary Winter Park proper and the newer, flashier Mary Jane. With 52 trails and 800 acres of spectacular skiing terrain, both offer an excellent variety of slopes for beginners or experts at some of the lowest lift prices in the state.

The Winter Park Ski School is almost as renowned as the mountain it's conducted on. With a staff of 150 expert instructors, the school keeps up with every new skiing technique for all ages and skills. If you're looking for greater challenge, there's the Competition Center with programs for ballet, aerials, racing, and jumping.

Equally known and loved is Winter Park's handicapped ski program which has helped thousands of courageous people enjoy the joys of skiing.

Other skiing challenges include NASTAR and head-to-head slalom races. Winter Park is also the site for several other competitive events, including the First of Denver Cup. For a zanier time, don't miss special events

like the Winter Carnival, and the Land Tuna Cup.

Take a moonlight hay ride, snowmobile, or ride to the mountaintop in a snow cat. You might also consider cross-country skiing nearby at the magnificently groomed trails of Devil's Thumb Ranch.

Summer too is fun at Winter Park, especially with the Alpine Slide traversing down the mountain. There are chairlift rides, jeep tours, golfing, horseback riding, and backpacking through some of the most beautiful scenery in the state.

No matter what time of the year you visit Winter Park, there are plenty of facilities with cafeterias, restaurant and bar, ski shops, and ample parking.

PORTS OF CALL

Picture this: More than 800 people signing up to go on a vacation trip, paying about $800 each and without even knowing where they're going!

But all of them know *who* is taking them on this trip, and that makes a world of difference. In this case, *who* is the Ports of Call Travel Club.

As Larry Turrill, executive director of Ports of Call, says, "They don't care where they're going. For six days and five nights, they know they're going to have a ball!"

Ports of Call is one of five travel clubs in the country. Its almost 23 thousand memberships translates into more than 60 thousand people, making Ports of Call as large as the other four travel clubs combined.

What makes Ports of Call so appealing? Convenience, economy, service, worry-free worldwide travel. You drop off your luggage at a special Ports of Call terminal on the southern edge of Stapleton International Airport and climb aboard one of the eight airliners in the club's private fleet. The next time you see your bag is in the hotel room at your destination.

Ports of Call offers "mystery trips" as well as hundreds of published destinations throughout the United States and around the globe. Places like Las Vegas, Disneyland, Manzanillo, Bermuda, Kenya, Spain, Scandinavia, Russia, Morocco, and Egypt.

More than 125 Ports of Call employees are dedicated to making travel as trouble-free as possible, whether your trip is a Las Vegas weekend or 16 days in Europe.

The opportunity to see the world is something most people just dream about. Ports of Call turns those dreams into a happy real-life experience.

Index

Printing
Frederic Printing, Denver, Colorado

Typesetting
The Composing Room, Denver, Colorado

Color Separations
Capitol Engraving Company, Denver, Colorado

Special thanks to
Evelyn Weingardt, Scottie Maxwell, David Wood,
David Weinstein, Cindy Varner, Mayor William McNichols,
Beverly St. John, Mr. and Mrs. John Topping, Sr.,
and Bruce B. Paul, Publisher's Assistant